BRITISH GEOLOGICAL SL

British Regional Geology

London and the Thames Valley

FOURTH EDITION

Compiled by M G Sumbler, MA

LONDON   HMSO   1996

HMSO

HMSO publications are available from:

HMSO Publications Centre
(Mail, fax and telephone orders only)
PO Box 276, London SW8 5DT
Telephone orders 0171-873 9090
General enquiries 0171-873 0011
Queuing system in operation for both
numbers
Fax orders 0171-873 8200

HMSO Bookshops
49 High Holborn, London WC1V 6HB
(counter service only)
0171-873 0011   Fax 0171-831 1326
68–69 Bull Street, Birmingham B4 6AD
0121-236 9696   Fax 0121-236 9699
33 Wine Street, Bristol BS1 2BQ
0117-9264306   Fax 0117-9294515
9 Princess Street, Manchester M60 8AS
0161-834 7201   Fax 0161-833 0634
16 Arthur Street, Belfast BT1 4GD
01232-238451   Fax 01232-235401
71 Lothian Road, Edinburgh EH3 9AZ
0131-228 4181   Fax 0131-229 2734
HMSO Oriel Bookshop, The Friary,
Cardiff CF1 4AA
01222-395548   Fax 01222-384347

HMSO's Accredited Agents
(see Yellow Pages)

And through good booksellers

BRITISH GEOLOGICAL SURVEY

Keyworth, Nottingham NG12 5GG
0115-936 3100

Murchison House, West Mains Road,
Edinburgh, EH9 3LA   0131-667 1000

London Information Office, Natural
History Museum, Earth Galleries,
Exhibition Road, London SW7 2DE
0171-589 4090

The full range of Survey publications is
available through the Sales Desks at
Keyworth and at Murchison House,
Edinburgh, and in the BGS London
Information Office in the Natural
History Museum (Earth Galleries). The
adjacent bookshop stocks the more
popular books for sale over the counter.
Most BGS books and reports can be
bought from HMSO and through
HMSO agents and retailers. Maps are
listed in the BGS Map Catalogue, and
can be bought together with books and
reports through BGS-approved stockists
and agents as well as direct from BGS.

The British Geological Survey carries out the
geological survey of Great Britain and
Northern Ireland (the latter as an agency
service for the government of Northern
Ireland), and of the surrounding continental
shelf, as well as its basic research projects. It
also undertakes programmes of British
technical aid in geology in developing
countries as arranged by the Overseas Devel-
opment Administration.

The British Geological Survey is a component
body of the Natural Environment Research
Council.

Bibliographic reference

SUMBLER, M G. 1996.   *British regional*
geology: London and the Thames Valley
(4th edition).   (London: HMSO for the
British Geological Survey.)

Maps and diagrams in this book use topography based on Ordnance Survey
mapping

Contents

Figures   Page

Plates

Tables   Page

Foreword to fourth edition

The first edition of this guide was published in 1935. Subsequent editions with modest revisions appeared in 1947 and 1960. Since that time, a vast amount of geological research has been carried out by the British Geological Survey, and by academic and industrial researchers. This work has ranged from surface mapping, to the investigation of deep structures by means of boreholes and geophysical techniques. The changes in our geological understanding of the region have been so great that the guide has been entirely rewritten.

The London and Thames Valley region includes some of the most densely populated and urbanised parts of the United Kingdom. To many people in such an environment, the relevance of geology may not be apparent. However, geology is more than just an interesting aspect of natural history; it has been crucial to the development of the region in many respects. Geology controls the form of the landscape on which we live, and our most basic needs are acquired from geological sources, from the bricks and concrete of our houses to the water we drink.

This book gives a comprehensive account of the geological development of the region, the succession of the rocks, and the uses to which they are put. It begins with the most ancient rocks, present at depth and known only from deep boreholes. Of the rocks which can be seen at the surface, the oldest are the Jurassic strata of the Cotswold Hills, well known to the fossil collector and the source of some fine building stones in the capital. These rocks, like much of the overlying strata including the chalk of the downlands, were laid down in warm tropical seas. Such environments were very different from those represented by the sands, gravels and clays from the most recent part of the geological timescale. Of these, the deposits of the River Thames record the climatic fluctuations of the Pleistocene 'Ice Age' in a completeness and detail which is unique in onshore Britain. Flint implements found at many sites, chronicle the colonisation of the region by human beings. The muds and peats laid down in the Thames estuary during the last few thousand years, give evidence of gradual sinking of the land, which is continuing to the present day. The recognition of this process is one factor which led to the construction of flood defences such as the Thames Barrier, and is a positive demonstration of the way that geological research is essential to safeguard our way of life.

This account is written for all those who have an interest in their surroundings. It is intended especially for the amateur geologist or student, but will also help those concerned with planning, civil engineering or the extractive industries who need a summary of our geological knowledge. It will also be of value to the experienced professional geologist, for this book has been written by authors who are acknowledged experts in their fields, and there is much information within these covers that has never been published before.

Peter J Cook, CBE, DSc, FGS, CGeol
Director,
British Geological Survey
Kingsley Dunham Centre
Keyworth
Nottingham NG12 5GG

June 1996

ACKNOWLEDGEMENTS

The range of geological topics encompassed in this guide is great, and in order to produce a balanced and comprehensive text within a reasonable timescale, the help of many individuals has been enlisted, both from within the BGS and from elsewhere in the geological community. Each of the chapters has been written by geologists with many years of experience in the relevant topics, and in many cases includes information that has not hitherto been published. Particularly, thanks are due to those authors from outside the BGS, namely Dr D R Bridgland (University of Durham), Dr H G Owen (formerly The National History Museum, London), Dr J E Robinson (University College, London), Mr C J Wood (Scops Geological Services, Croydon) and Dr J J Wymer (Great Cressingham, Thetford), who have generously given their time. The guide has been compiled by M G Sumbler, assisted by Dr B M Cox, who was largely responsible for designing the plates of fossils, and the numerous tables and diagrams. It has been edited by Drs R W Gallois, A A Jackson and Mr R D Lake.

Table 1 Main stratal divisions and rock types represented in the London and Thames Valley region.

ERATHEM	SYSTEM	SERIES	AGE (MILLION YEARS BP)	PRINCIPAL DEPOSITS
CAINOZOIC	QUATERNARY	HOLOCENE	0.01	Alluvium, hillwash, tufa, peat, coastal and estuarine sand and mud
		PLEISTOCENE		River terrace sand and gravel; glacial till, sand and gravel; slope deposits, clay-with-flints, loess
	NEOGENE		1.64 / 23	RED CRAG and NORWICH CRAG: shallow-marine sand
	PALAEOGENE		65	BAGSHOT FORMATION, BARTON BEDS and BRACKLESHAM BEDS: mainly marine sand; THAMES GROUP (including LONDON CLAY): marine mudstone LAMBETH GROUP: shallow marine sand; fluvial and estuarine mud and sand
MESOZOIC	CRETACEOUS	UPPER	97	CHALK GROUP: marine, coccolith-rich limestone (chalk)
		LOWER	146	GAULT and UPPER GREENSAND FORMATIONS: marine mudstone, siltstone and sandstone; LOWER GREENSAND GROUP: shallow-marine sand and sandstone; WEALDEN GROUP: fluviatile and non-marine sandstone, siltstone and mudstone
	JURASSIC	UPPER	157	PORTLAND and PURBECK FORMATIONS: marine and lagoonal limestone and sand; CORALLIAN GROUP: marine limestone and sandstone; ANCHOLME GROUP: marine mudstone
		MIDDLE	178	INFERIOR and GREAT OOLITE GROUPS: marine limestone with some mudstone and sandstone; nonmarine facies in east
		LOWER	208	LIAS GROUP: marine mudstone with sandstone and ironstone
	TRIASSIC		245	PENARTH GROUP: marine mudstone, limestone and sandstone MERCIA MUDSTONE GROUP: wind-blown and lacustrine mudstone and siltstone with some fluvial sandstone SHERWOOD SANDSTONE GROUP: fluvial sandstone
PALAEOZOIC	PERMIAN		290	Desert—probably no sediment preserved
	CARBONI-FEROUS		362	Deltaic and coastal mudstone and sandstone with coals Volcanic rocks Limestone and mudstone
	DEVONIAN		408	Continental, lacustrine and fluvial mudstone, siltstone and sandstone (Old Red Sandstone), with some marine mudstone, siltstone and limestone
	SILURIAN		439	Marine mudstone, sandstone and limestone
	ORDOVICIAN		510	Marine mudstone with minor sandstone
	CAMBRIAN		570	Marine mudstone and sandstone
PRE-CAMBRIAN				Volcanic rocks of Withycombe Farm Borehole, Banbury

Not to scale. Pre-Jurassic strata are known only from boreholes. The rock record is very incomplete; long intervals are unrepresented by rocks within this region.

1   Introduction

The region described in this guide covers a large part of southern England, with Greater London at its heart (Figure 1). From its westernmost point in the Cotswold Hills near Chippenham, the northern margin of the region follows the boundaries of Wiltshire, Oxfordshire, Buckinghamshire, Bedford-shire, Hertfordshire and Essex, to meet the North Sea coast at Harwich. Bed-fordshire, excluded from previous editions of this guide, is now added to complete the geological picture. The southern limit of the region cuts across Wiltshire to the neighbourhood of Marlborough, then follows geological boundary lines (the base of the Cainozoic and of the Chalk Group), to near Rochester in Kent, where the boundary follows the River Medway to meet the Thames estuary at the Isle of Grain.

The geological succession represented in the region is shown in Table 1, and a simplified map of the geology is shown in Figure 1. This map shows the outcrop of 'Solid' (i.e. bedrock) strata, and the areas where the solid rocks are concealed by younger 'drift' (mainly unconsolidated deposits Quaternary age). The oldest rocks of the region, proved in boreholes, are Precambrian and Palaeozoic formations, which are seen at the surface elsewhere in England and Wales. They form a basement complex that lies at depths of over 1.5 km in the west and south of the region and forms the much shallower London Platform elsewhere (Figure 2).

The solid rocks that crop out in the region are of Mesozoic and Cainozoic age. Their outcrop pattern is closely related to the geological structure. This is dominated by the London Basin, which takes the form of a broad, gentle, synclinal fold, open to the east. Its axis can be traced from Marlborough in the west, through Newbury, Chertsey, and north London, to beyond the coast of Essex (Figure 1). The oldest rocks at surface are found at the edge of the syncline, with progressively younger ones towards the centre (Figure 2).

On the north-western limb of this main fold, the rocks dip gently and uniformly to the south-east, generally at less than one degree. As a conse-quence, the outcrops of the different rock units form subparallel bands that trend approximately south-west to north-east. They comprise units which are alternately more and less resistant to erosion, and this gives a characteristic 'grain' to the countryside (Figure 3); the harder beds form ranges of hills and the softer beds the intervening vales.

The oldest rocks seen at outcrop belong to the Lias Group of Early Jurassic age. The outcrop is restricted to the north-west of the region (Figure 1). This group is described more fully in the guides for the adjoining Bristol and Gloucester, and Central England regions. It is dominated by mudstone which is poorly exposed, but also includes the Marlstone, which forms prominent escarpments around Banbury, and was once an important source of iron ore.

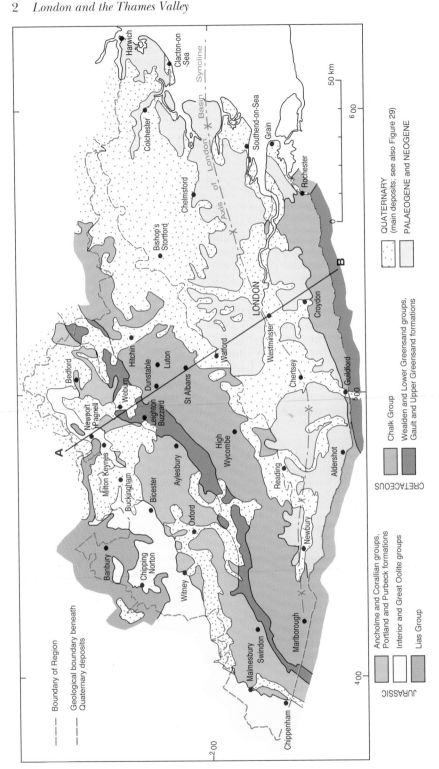

Boundary of Region

Geological boundary beneath
Quaternary deposits

QUATERNARY
(main deposits; see also Figure 29)

PALAEOGENE and NEOGENE

CRETACEOUS

Chalk Group

Wealden and Lower Greensand groups,
Gault and Upper Greensand formations

JURASSIC

Ancholme and Corallian groups,
Portland and Purbeck formations

Inferior and Great Oolite groups

Lias Group

50 km

The succeeding Inferior and Great Oolite groups, of Mid Jurassic age, are dominated by limestones. These strata form the landscape of the north Cotswolds, characterised by open upland areas dissected by narrow valleys and with picturesque villages built of local stone. The rocks are commonly highly fossiliferous, and can yield many attractive specimens to the collector.

South-east of the Cotswolds, the Ancholme Group is of Mid to Late Jurassic age. It consists predominantly of mudstone that forms a belt of low-lying country passing through Oxford and Milton Keynes. The Oxford Clay, in the lower part, remains the premier resource of brick-clay and is actively worked from large pits near Bedford. In Oxfordshire, and to the south-west, the Corallian Group, of Late Jurassic age intervenes in the middle of this mudstone succession. It is dominated by limestone and sandstone which, being more resistant to erosion, form an attractive belt of hills. Locally, the beds yield beautiful fossil corals, which were once found in abundance in quarries near Oxford. Above the Ancholme Group, the youngest part of the Jurassic sequence is represented by the Portland and Purbeck formations, which cap the prominent hills on which Swindon and Aylesbury are built. Giant ammonites from the Portland Formation can be seen in the walls of local buildings.

The Cretaceous succession begins with the Wealden Group. At outcrop, this is represented only by small remnants of the Whitchurch Sand Formation, which overlies the Portland and Purbeck beds at Swindon and between Oxford and Aylesbury. At depth, in the extreme south-east of the region, the group is more complete and much thicker. The succeeding Lower Greensand is also rather patchy in its distribution. It is thickest and best developed in Bedfordshire, where it is quarried extensively for sand and fuller's earth. Numerous quarries near Leighton Buzzard display a wealth of sedimentary structures. The overlying Gault Formation is dominated by mudstone which forms the low-lying ground of the Vale of White Horse and the Vale of Aylesbury (Figure 3). The basal beds are seen as overburden in the sand pits around Leighton Buzzard. Above the Gault, the Upper Greensand forms a low escarpment in Wiltshire and Oxfordshire.

A far more impressive scarp is formed by the Chalk Group, of Late Cretaceous age. The Chalk has an extensive outcrop, and forms the Marlborough and Berkshire Downs, and the Chiltern Hills (Figure 3). It is also present in the south of the region forming the North Downs, which constitute the southern rim of the London Basin (Plate 1). The chalk downlands form the highest ground of the region, with large areas over 180 m above Ordnance Datum (OD) and a high point of 277 m above OD at Liddington Castle, south-east of Swindon. These downlands provide open countryside within easy reach of the major conurbations and are increasingly important as amenity areas. Commercially, the chalk is important as a source of raw material for cement manufacture, but its greatest value is as an aquifer; much of the water used for public supply in the region is pumped from the Chalk.

Above the Chalk, the central part of the London Basin is infilled with Palaeogene deposits, dominated by sand and mudstone. The London Clay

Figure 1 Geological sketch map of the London and Thames Valley region. For cross-section A–B, see Figure 2.

Plate 1   The escarpment of the North Downs at Box Hill, near Dorking in Surrey. Formed by the Chalk Group, it marks the southern boundary of the region (A9938).

Formation is the thickest and most widespread of the mudstone formations. It is particularly important to the engineer, for much of London is built on it, and many kilometres of tunnels beneath the capital are excavated within it.

The London Basin syncline developed mainly during the late Palaeogene and early Neogene periods, in response to more dramatic earth movements in southern Europe, where major folds and thrust faults were forming the Alps. These movements caused uplift of much of Britain and the whole of the region became dry land for the first time since the Triassic Period. Rivers developed, including an ancestor of the Thames, and for many millions of years during the latter part of the Neogene Period they gradually sculpted a landscape, which in its overall form bore some resemblance to the one we see today.

Quaternary deposits or 'drift', give an important insight into the events of the most recent geological past. These predominantly unconsolidated deposits

Figure 2   Geological sketch cross-section across the region, showing the form of the London Basin syncline, and the thick Jurassic and Lower Cretaceous successions in the buried Wessex Basin (right). Note the great exaggeration of the vertical scale; for example, the true dip of the base of the Chalk Group on the north-west limb of the syncline is approximately 0.5°, and that on the south-eastern limb is approximately 1.5°. For comparative purposes, the clock tower of the Houses of Parliament ('Big Ben') is 96 m high, and is drawn to the correct vertical scale. See Figure 1 for line of section.

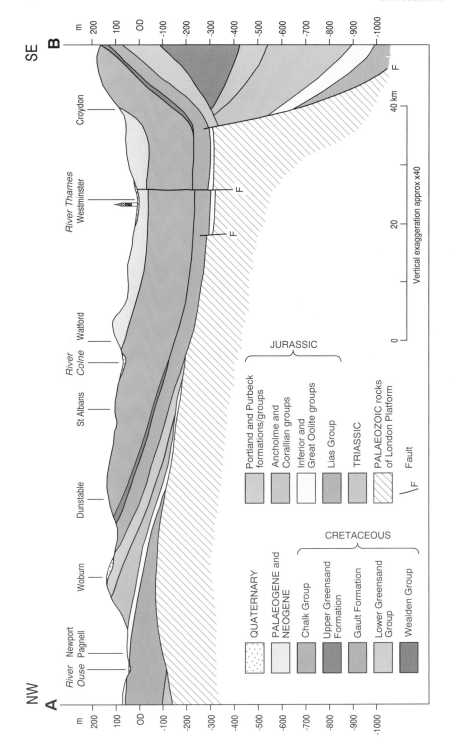

may be many metres thick and cover large areas (Figures 1 and 29), concealing the outcrop of solid rocks. They are of critical importance to the civil engineer and also include valuable resources of sand and gravel for the construction industry. Quaternary deposits of the region include a great variety of materials, which formed in many different geological environments. The most widespread are the deposits of the Thames and other rivers, which are dominated by sand and gravel. Also important are glacial deposits, which blanket much of the north-eastern part of the region; these are a legacy of the Anglian Ice Age which occurred nearly half a million years ago, when glaciers advanced as far south as London. This modified the landscape dramatically, diverting the River Thames southwards into its present course. Other Quaternary deposits include Clay-with-Flints, which covers much of the high ground of the Chalk outcrop, and solifluxion material, which is almost ubiquitous in valleys and on the lower slopes of the hills.

The rocks which crop out in the region are all sedimentary in origin and all contain fossils in greater or lesser abundance. Specimens from this region, and elsewhere, can be seen in the Natural History Museum in South Kensington. Another venue in the capital where geology comes to life is Crystal Palace Park in south-east London where, in the nineteenth century, an attempt was made to reconstruct the geological history of Britain. Much of the display can still be seen; it includes the first life-size reconstructions of dinosaurs, made between 1852 and 1854.

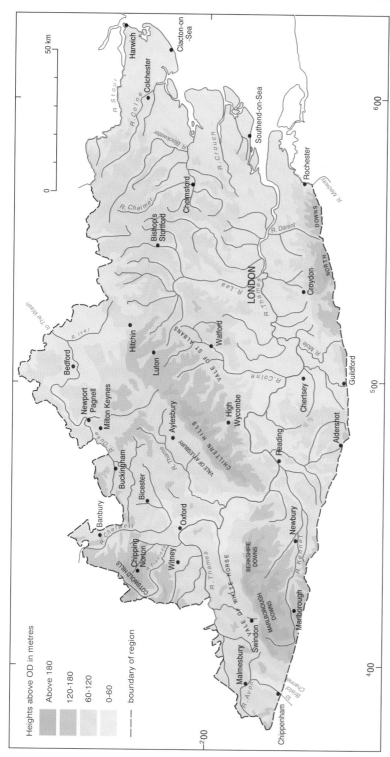

Figure 3 Sketch map showing major topographical features of the region. Comparison with Figure 1 demonstrates the strong relationship between topography and geology.

2   Concealed rocks and basement structure

PRECAMBRIAN AND PALAEOZOIC BASEMENT

Deep boreholes, drilled for oil, coal and gas exploration, water abstraction
or scientific research have shown that Mesozoic and younger rocks rest
upon a 'basement' of Precambrian and Palaeozoic (Cambrian to Permian)
rocks which have undergone a long and complicated history. These
basement rocks are similar to those which crop out in Wales, parts of the
Midlands, and northern England. Their distribution, beneath the Mesozoic
cover, is shown in Figure 4. Generally, they lie at great depth, being over
1.5 km deep in parts of the west and south of the region (Figure 5).
Throughout the central and eastern parts, they lie at much shallower
depth, forming the 'London Platform'. This is some 300 m deep beneath
Central London and it may be less than 100 m beneath the surface in parts
of Oxfordshire, Buckinghamshire and Bedfordshire (Figures 2, 5 and 6).

Precambrian

Precambrian rocks are probably present at great depth beneath the entire
region, but they have been proved only near Banbury, where Withycombe
Farm Borehole penetrated basaltic andesite lavas, at over 1 km depth (Figure
6). Geochemically similar volcanic rocks are known from Charnwood Forest
in Leicestershire, and the rocks from Withycombe Farm are probably likewise
of late Precambrian age, between 600 and 700 million years (Ma) old. They
were formed in island arc and basin complexes.

Cambrian and Ordovician

By the dawn of the Cambrian Period, the region lay on the northern margin
of a supercontinent known as Gondwana. Deeper water of the Iapetus and
Tornquist oceans lay to the north (Figure 7A). Because of the movement of
crustal plates, these oceans gradually narrowed throughout the early Palaeozoic (Cambrian to early Devonian). The associated episodes of uplift and subsidence, folding, faulting and volcanicity are ascribed to the Caledonian
Orogeny. This had a major influence on the geological history of the London
and Thames Valley region.

Cambrian and Ordovician rocks have been proved immediately below the
Mesozoic cover in several areas (Figure 4), and they probably underlie younger
Palaeozoic strata throughout most of the region. The Cambrian strata were laid
down in a relatively shallow shelf sea over the Midland Platform (Figure 7A),
and generally the succession is thin. In Withycombe Farm Borehole, Cambrian

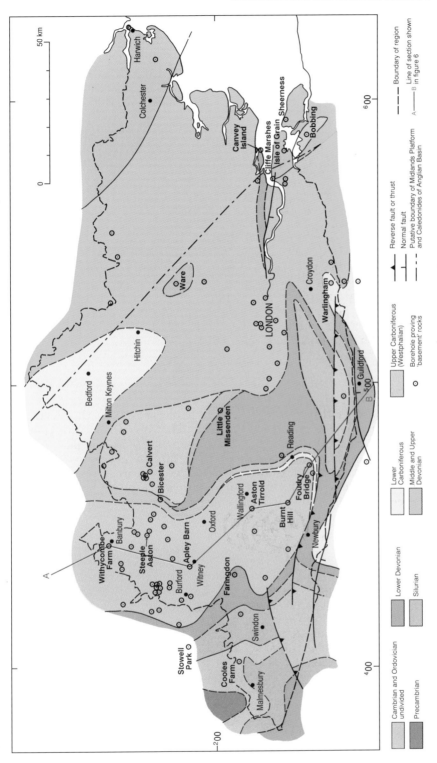

Figure 4   Sketch map showing the distribution of Precambrian and Palaeozoic 'basement' rocks beneath Mesozoic cover.

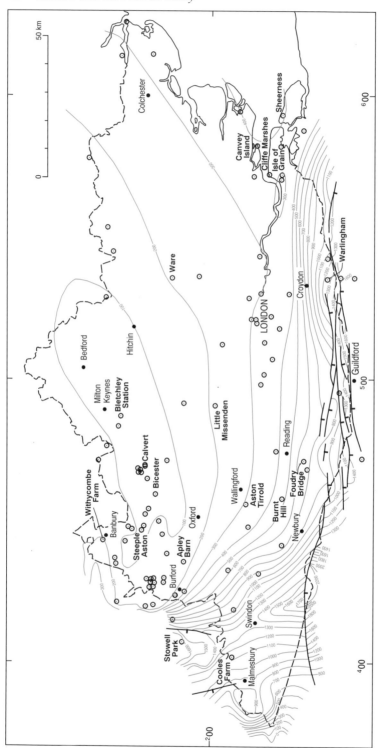

Figure 5   Contours on the surface of the Precambrian and Palaeozoic 'basement'. Contours in metres *below* Ordnance Datum.

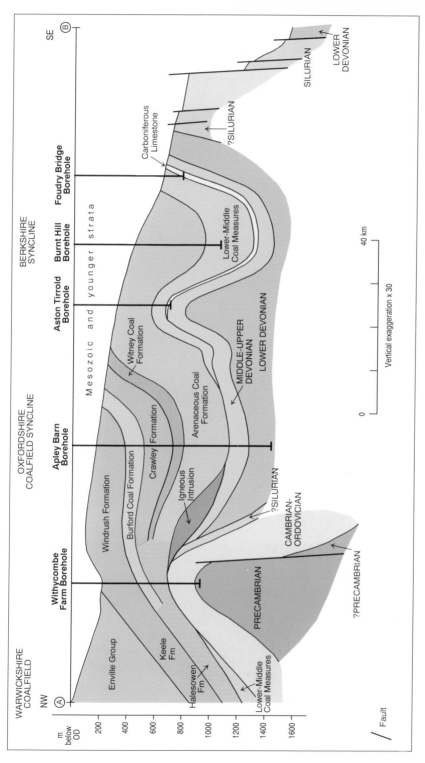

Figure 6 Generalised cross-section of the Palaeozoic strata in the western part of the region. For line of section see Figure 4.

strata, totalling 194 m in thickness, comprise grey, green and purple, silty mudstones with thin limestone beds. This succession is Lower Cambrian, any younger Cambrian strata having been removed by erosion prior to deposition of the overlying Carboniferous beds. Cooles Farm Borehole near Malmesbury, terminated in about 170 m of Upper Cambrian mudstones and sandstones.

In early Ordovician (Tremadoc) times, parts of the region were subjected to relatively rapid subsidence, and thick accumulations of sediment built up locally; for example, Cooles Farm Borehole penetrated over 2 km of Tremadocian strata. Much of the Cambrian and Ordovician shown in Figure 4, belongs to the Tremadoc Series. This has been proved in a number of boreholes between Bicester and Milton Keynes, where the strata are dominated by graptolitic mudstone with minor sandstones. Locally, the beds are strongly folded, and steeply dipping or vertical beds have been encountered in some boreholes. At Calvert, the strata are intruded by basic igneous sills.

No late Ordovician strata are known in the region. They may be absent, perhaps because of uplift and emergence associated with an episode of calc-alkaline volcanism which occurred to the north at this time (Figure 7B). However, sandy shales of late Ordovician (Caradoc) age have been proved at Bobbing, Kent, just south of the region.

Silurian

Boreholes have proved Silurian strata beneath the Mesozoic cover in parts of the region (Figure 4), and elsewhere they may be present beneath Devonian rocks. Throughout the Silurian Period, the western part of the region (the Midland Platform of Figure 7C) formed a shallow shelf sea, in which calcareous mud, sand and carbonates were deposited. These beds are commonly highly fossiliferous, with abundant brachiopods, bivalves, gastropods, trilobites and crinoids. Strata ranging from early (Llandovery) to late (Přídolí) Silurian age are known, but individual borehole sequences are incomplete and the total thickness of the Silurian succession is unknown. There is evidence of volcanic activity in the west of the region in early Silurian times. At Bicester, probable Llandovery sandstones rest on volcanic rocks similar to those cropping out at Tortworth in Gloucestershire, to the west of the region. Mid Silurian strata are known from a borehole at Cliffe Marshes in north Kent, which proved calcareous, shelly mudstones, very similar to the Wenlock Shales of the Welsh borders. Mudstones, limestones and sandstones of Wenlock age were also proved at Ware, Hertfordshire. At Little Missenden, near Amersham, grey shales, and sandy and shelly limestones are of Přídolí age.

The Silurian shelf sea was bounded to the north-east by deeper water of the Anglian Basin where muds and silts accumulated (Figure 7C). These sediments, now seen as slates and greywacke sandstones, are known from boreholes at Sheerness, the Isle of Grain and near Harwich. The change in facies between the shelf and basin is analogous to that seen in the Silurian of the Welsh borders.

Figure 7   Sketch maps illustrating the generalised palaeogeography of southern England through the Palaeozoic Era.

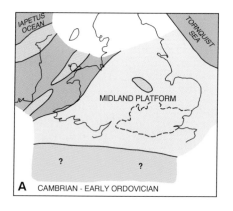

A CAMBRIAN - EARLY ORDOVICIAN

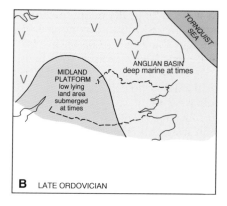

B LATE ORDOVICIAN

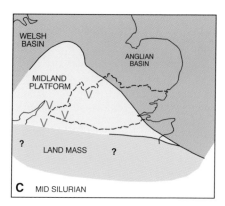

C MID SILURIAN

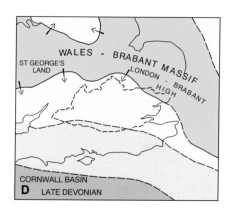

D LATE DEVONIAN

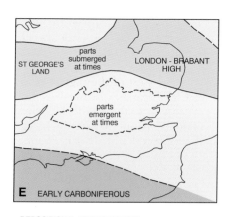

E EARLY CARBONIFEROUS

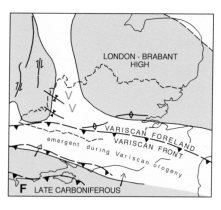

F LATE CARBONIFEROUS

DEPOSITIONAL ENVIRONMENTS

Emergent area, net erosion or non-deposition

Shallow marine deposition

Clastic input

Alluvial, coastal, deltaic or nearshore marine environment

Deeper marine deposition

V Volcanicity

TECTONIC FEATURES

Thrust fault

Anticline

Boundary of region

Transcurrent fault

Syncline

Devonian

In early to mid-Devonian times, the closure of the Iapetus Ocean, to the north of the region, marked the culmination of the Caledonian Orogeny. The geography of the region, and indeed of Europe, was transformed. The rocks of the Ordovician–Silurian basins were deformed and uplifted to form highland areas. The deformed 'Caledonides', best known from Wales and Scotland, are present at depth in the eastern part of the region, where the Silurian rocks of the Anglian Basin are strongly folded and cleaved. The Midland Platform formed a stable block which was relatively unaffected by the earth movements. The junction of the two tectonic regimes along the eastern margin of the platform (Figure 7C) probably represents a major fault system comparable with that seen in the Welsh borders. Erosion of the newly created highland area, the Wales–Brabant Massif, provided sediment which was deposited on the former Midland Platform, now a low-lying plain with an ocean to the south (Figure 7D).

Devonian strata underlie a large part of the region. In addition to the areas shown in Figure 4, they are also present beneath the Carboniferous strata of Oxfordshire, Bedfordshire and elsewhere (Figure 6). The deposits are predominantly of continental 'Old Red Sandstone' facies, and include desert, lacustrine and fluvial sediments. Fossils are rare, although fragments of fish occur in some of the fluvial sandstones. In parts of the region, sedimentary rocks of coastal, nearshore and shallow-marine origin are also present. No borehole has proved a complete Devonian sequence; 509 m were proved at Willesden in west London, but the total thickness is probably considerably more. Geophysical evidence suggests that the succession thickens westwards across Oxfordshire, and also southwards into the Weald. It may also thicken beneath the Thames estuary.

The oldest part of the succession, assigned to the **Lower Old Red Sandstone**, is essentially of early Devonian age, but may include latest Silurian (Přídolí) beds at the base. The strata, known from Faringdon and Witney in the west of the region, from Beckton in east London and from Canvey Island, are dominated by red, green and purple fluvial sandstones, with shale, siltstone and silty mudstone beds. They are very similar to the Lower Old Red Sandstone seen at outcrop in the Welsh borders.

The later part of the Early Devonian was a time of deformation, uplift and erosion, representing the final phase of the Caledonian Orogeny. Consequently, the **Upper Old Red Sandstone**, of late Mid and Late Devonian age, rests unconformably on the Lower Old Red Sandstone and oversteps onto Silurian and Tremadoc strata in the east and central parts of the region (Figures 4 and 6). Many boreholes have penetrated these beds, particularly in the London area. The strata include a variety of rocks, overall dominated by red to purple silty mudstone and green sandstone mainly of fluvial origin. In addition, some boreholes have proved marine mudstone, siltstone and limestone, some containing rich faunas of bivalves and brachiopods; these beds, similar to parts of the Devonian succession of south Devon and Cornwall, indicate a temporary incursion of the sea, which extended northwards across the whole region in the early part of Late Devonian times.

Carboniferous

A marine transgression during early Carboniferous times, once again transformed the region into a shallow shelf sea, bordering a deeper ocean to the south (Figure 7E). Lower Carboniferous (Dinantian) rocks have been proved by a few boreholes, but the successions are thin and incomplete, due principally to subsequent erosion. The rocks proved are similar to those in the Mendips and South Wales.

In Warlingham Borehole, south of Croydon, over 150 m of oolitic limestones and shales are of earliest Carboniferous (Courceyan) age. Lower Carboniferous, argillaceous, shelly limestones and silty mudstones proved at Aston Tirrold near Wallingford and Foudry Bridge, south of Reading (Figure 6), are respectively of Courceyan and Holkerian age.

From mid Carboniferous to early Permian times, closure of the ocean to the south was associated with gradual deformation and eventually northward-directed thrusting in southern England. These earth movements, known as the Variscan Orogeny (Figure 7F), modified the geography of the region, uplifting the sea floor of earlier Carboniferous times to form, initially, an area of predominantly nonmarine deposition, and finally dry land. No rocks dating from the earliest (Namurian) part of the Late Carboniferous (Silesian) are known in the region, probably because of uplift and erosion. In the west, later Silesian (Westphalian) Coal Measures rest unconformably on Dinantian or older strata. These Coal Measures are preserved in a syncline beneath Mesozoic cover between Banbury, Burford and Reading (Figures 4 and 6). Their limited extent is a result of later erosion, and Coal Measures may originally have extended from Kent to South Wales. They were deposited in a deltaic and coastal environment adjacent to the southern margin of a landmass, the London–Brabant High (Figure 7F). The rocks are mainly siltstones and mudstones with some coals, seatearths and thin sandstones. However, basic volcanic and intrusive rocks locally dominate the sequence. In Steeple Aston Borehole, between Banbury and Oxford, a complex dolerite sill, 165 m thick, separates the Coal Measures from the underlying Devonian strata (Figure 6).

The **Lower and Middle Coal Measures**, Langsettian (Westphalian A) to Duckmantian (Westphalian B) in age, are present only in the south of the basin, and are unconformably overlain by **Upper Coal Measures** of Bolsovian (Westphalian C) and Westphalian D age. The most complete succession of Upper Coal Measures, 959 m thick, was proved in Apley Barn Borehole near Witney, close to the axis of the syncline (Figure 6). The beds thin northwards and pass into the Halesowen and Keele formations of the Warwickshire Coalfield. The basal part of the Upper Coal Measures comprises the Arenaceous Coal Formation, mainly of early Westphalian D age. This formation consists mainly of greenish grey, cross-bedded, coarse-grained sandstones, but also includes the thickest coal seam (1.5 m) proved in the region. Above, the succession consists of grey coal-bearing strata (the Witney Coal and Burford Coal formations), alternating with red beds (the Crawley and Windrush formations). The grey beds show rhythmic sedimentation, with a typical cycle consisting of mudstone passing up into sandstone, which is capped by a seat-earth and a thin coal. These cycles indicate a prograding delta environment, with deposition in progressively shallower water, and eventual emergence and growth of forest vegetation. Fossil plants are abundant, and some mudstones contain nonmarine bivalves and other fossils. In the upper part of the Burford Coal Formation, thin limestone beds containing *Spirorbis* worm tubes are found in place of the coals. These may have been deposited in shallow lakes. The red beds, mainly mudstones, are probably mostly fluvial in origin, formed in a generally arid environment.

The final phases of the Variscan Orogeny took place in latest Carboniferous times. Geophysical research has shown that the northernmost folds and thrusts of the Variscan fold belt (the 'Variscan Front') lie in the southernmost part of the region (Figures 4 and 7F). Within the Variscan fold belt, the Palaeozoic basement suffered pervasive deformation, being strongly folded and cut by major east-to-west-trending thrusts. North of the Variscan front, the region was barely affected, although some broad, large-scale folds such as the Oxfordshire Coalfield Syncline were formed at this time, and the whole region was uplifted to become land.

Permian

During the Permian Period, the region was probably a rocky desert. Within the region, no deposits are known from this period, although it is possible that in the west, alluvial deposits may have begun to accumulate in the developing Worcester Basin. In boreholes, the uppermost parts of the Palaeozoic successions are commonly mottled with purplish, reddish and ochreous colours which result from Permian and Triassic desert weathering.

CONCEALED MESOZOIC ROCKS

The overall structural framework of the region (Figure 8) was largely developed by the close of the Palaeozoic Era. It had a profound effect on later sedimentation patterns. The London Platform underlies most of the eastern part of the region and is part of the London–Brabant Massif. This remained as a relatively stable structural high throughout the Mesozoic Era. Northwards, the platform merges with the East Midlands Shelf, an area of restricted subsidence marginal to the Southern North Sea Basin, where thicker sedimentary sequences accumulated. Other deep, fault-bounded sediment traps, the Worcester Basin and the Wessex Basin, lay to the west and south respectively. The main elements of this structure are readily apparent from the form of the Palaeozoic basement surface (Figure 5).

The Mesozoic history of the region is essentially one of gradual, but discontinuous, sedimentary infill of the basins, and encroachment onto the London Platform. The platform probably did not become entirely buried until Cretaceous times.

Triassic

During the Triassic Period, the London Platform was an area of erosion, but sediments accumulated in the adjoining basins. Although only thin Triassic suc-

Figure 8   Mesozoic structural setting. The southern and, probably, the western boundaries of the London Platform are defined by basement faults, but the northern boundary with the East Midlands Shelf and North Sea Basin is gradational and arbitrary.

cessions are preserved in the eastern part of the Wessex Basin (Weald Basin), subsidence of the Worcester and western Wessex basins allowed a thick accumulation of sediment to build up. In Cooles Farm Borehole, sited on the axis of the Worcester Basin (Figures 8 and 9), 595 m of Triassic sedimentary rocks have been proved, and in Stowell Park Borehole, just to the north-west of the region, nearly 750 m of Triassic beds were penetrated without reaching the bottom of the succession. Other boreholes and geophysical evidence show that the succession thins markedly eastwards, towards the London Platform (Figure 9).

The Worcester Basin crosses the western part of the region (Figures 8 and 9), and the succession of strata there is very similar to that at outcrop farther

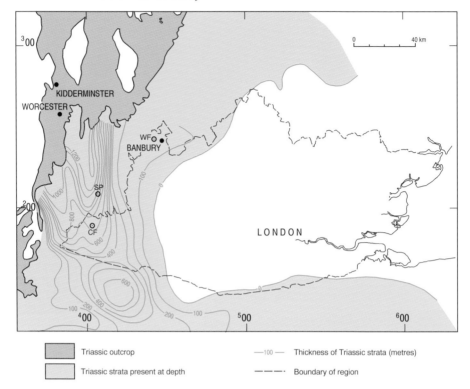

Figure 9   Distribution of Triassic strata CF = Cooles Farm Borehole; SP = Stowell Park Borehole; WF = Withycombe Farm Borehole.

north, between Worcester and Kidderminster. The lower part, 177m thick at Cooles Farm, comprises the **Sherwood Sandstone Group** of early to mid Triassic age. This consists mainly of fluviatile sandstones, with subordinate mudstone beds which represent floodplain deposits of the rivers. An arid climate can be inferred from the presence of nodules and beds of evaporitic anhydrite and gypsum within mudstone beds. The basal part of the Sherwood Sandstone includes conglomeratic beds, known as the **Kidderminster Formation** (formerly the Bunter Pebble Beds). These are characterised by rounded pebbles of quartzite and other hard rocks which can be matched with outcrops in Cornwall and north-western France; they were deposited by a large river flowing northwards through these areas. Overlying fluviatile sandstones probably include correlatives of the **Wildmoor Sandstone Formation** (formerly Upper Mottled Sandstone). The succeeding **Bromsgrove Sandstone Formation** (formerly Keuper Sandstone), extends beyond the older beds, lapping onto the western and north-western margins of the London Platform near Oxford and Bicester. The Bromsgrove Sandstone is dominated by medium- to fine-grained sandstone and silty mudstone. A bed with marine bivalves, ostracods and the brachiopod *Lingula* occurs in the upper part in Withycombe Farm Borehole. This indicates a temporary incursion of the sea which apparently entered the region from the north-east, around the northern margins of the London Platform. A mudstone bed with the small crustacean, *Euestheria*, known from other boreholes to the south-west of Withycombe Farm, may indicate a phase of brackish-water conditions.

The succeeding **Mercia Mudstone Group** (formerly Keuper Marl), is typically 300 to 400 m thick in the central part of the Worcester Basin. It overlaps the Bromsgrove Sandstone, encroaching onto the low-lying fringe areas of the London Platform, where thin sequences have been proved in boreholes to the north and north-east of Oxford. The Mercia Mudstone is dominated by reddish brown mudstone and siltstone; these are mainly composed of wind-blown dust, suggesting a generally arid climate. However, the presence of ripple marks and desiccation cracks indicates that some of the succession was deposited in water, probably in brackish lakes, replenished during occasional wet periods. As these lakes gradually dried up, evaporite minerals such as anhydrite and gypsum were deposited. These occur as layers and nodules at many horizons in the Mercia Mudstone. Thin beds of sandstone also occur sporadically and can be identified in borehole logs. Some of the sandstones can be correlated over wide areas and can also be traced to outcrop in the Midlands. They may represent deposits laid down in wadis or as sheets after sudden torrential storms. Generally, the Mercia Mudstone is devoid of fossils except for sporadic specimens of the crustacean *Euestheria* and rare footprints of early reptiles.

The thin **Blue Anchor Formation** at the top of the Mercia Mudstone Group comprises greenish grey, dolomitic mudstone and siltstone, with sporadic burrows, fish-scales and microfossils. These beds were probably deposited on coastal flats, occasionally flooded by the sea (sabkha). Within the region, the Blue Anchor Formation is probably restricted mainly to the Worcester Basin. Superficially similar deposits on the margins of the London Platform may include older parts of the Mercia Mudstone, originally deposited as red beds which were altered to a greenish colour in reducing conditions during Rhaetian or early Jurassic times.

The **Penarth Group**, of Rhaetian age, forms the topmost part of the Triassic succession. It is most completely developed in the central parts of the Worcester Basin, where it is up to about 20 m thick. The basal part comprises dark grey, shaly mudstone (Westbury Formation) which contains fossils including numerous bivalves such as *Rhaetavicula contorta*, indicating a shallow marine environment. These beds pass upwards into pale greenish grey silty mudstone (the **Cotham Member** of the **Lilstock Formation**) which reflects a temporary change to lagoonal conditions. Pure limestone above the mudstone was formerly known as the 'White Lias' and is now the **Langport Member** of the Lilstock Formation. It marks a return to fully marine conditions. In the Bicester area, the Penarth Group is represented by grey sandstones and thin limestones known as the **Twyford Beds**, which were laid down near the shoreline on the London Platform.

After a minor regression following the deposition of the Langport Member, marine conditions were once again established throughout the western part of the region by the end of Triassic times. This is indicated by a few metres of grey mudstone beds of Rhaetian age (the 'Pre-Planorbis Beds') at the base of the Lias Group in the Worcester Basin. Marine conditions persisted into Jurassic times, and indeed throughout most of the rest of the Mesozoic Era.

3 Jurassic: Introduction and Lias Group

INTRODUCTION TO THE JURASSIC

Jurassic rocks crop out in the north-western part of the region, from Chippenham to Bedfordshire (Figure 1). They are also present beneath more recent formations throughout the western half of the region and along the southern margin, almost as far north as the River Thames. They are absent beneath much of Greater London, north of the Thames, and to the north-east in Hertfordshire and Essex.

The Jurassic rocks (Table 2) were deposited over a period of about 70 million years, mainly in shallow shelf seas, and generally quite close to land. Much of the succession is made up of mudstone, commonly calcareous and finely silty. There are also substantial thicknesses of limestone and sandstone, mainly in the middle part of the succession. In the mid Jurassic, and again towards the end of the Jurassic, lagoonal and brackish to marine sediments were deposited in areas marginal to land.

Some Jurassic volcanicity occurred in the central North Sea and Western Approaches, associated with Atlantic sea-floor spreading, but no volcanic rocks are known in the Jurassic succession of this region. Minor, gentle folding and gradual movement along faults took place, principally along the margins of the London Platform, against the subsiding Worcester and Wessex basins (Figures 2 and 8), where the thickest sedimentary successions accumulated. With changing sea level, the London Platform varied from a land area of low relief, to a submerged shoal area. In general, successive Jurassic formations lapped farther onto the platform. Some, especially the younger formations, may have originally extended right across it, and were removed by erosion, during periods of low sea level, in later Jurassic or early Cretaceous times.

During the Jurassic, the region lay much closer to the equator than at present, and the climate was generally warm and humid. The seas were warm, with coral reefs and oolitic limestones forming at times. Many of the deposits are richly fossiliferous, with diverse faunas dominated by molluscs, especially bivalves, gastropods and cephalopods; brachiopods are also abundant in some beds (Plates 2, 3, 5, 7 and 8). The remains of marine reptiles and fish are also found at some horizons, and land vertebrates, including early mammals occur rarely. The ammonites are perhaps the most interesting and important of the Jurassic fossils. Their great diversity of form, and the rapidity of their evolutionary change provide the basis for chronostratigraphical classification, and enable correlation of strata on a worldwide scale. Jurassic time has been divided up into zones and subzones based on ammonites (Tables 3, 4 and 5). On average, an ammonite zone is thought to represent an interval of approximately one million years. Micro-

Table 2 Main stratal divisions of the Jurassic rocks of the region.

Epoch	Age (million years BP)	Chronostratigraphy		Lithostratigraphy		
		Series	Stage			
Late Jurassic	146	Upper Jurassic	Portlandian	Purbeck Formation		
				Portland Formation		
			Kimmeridgian	Ancholme		
			Oxfordian	Group	Corallian Group	
	157		Callovian			
Mid Jurassic		Middle Jurassic	Bathonian	Great Oolite Group		
			Bajocian	Inferior Oolite Group	Upper	
					Middle	
			Aalenian		Lower	
	178		Toarcian	Lias Group	Upper	
Early Jurassic		Lower Jurassic	Pliensbachian		Middle	
			Sinemurian		Lower	
			Hettangian			
	208					

Not to scale; non-sequences not shown.
The basal part of the Lias Group is of latest Triassic age.

fossils are also abundant, and both marine and land-derived forms are found. Of these, ostracods, foraminifera and dinoflagellate cysts can be used for zonation. These are particularly useful in those parts of the succession where ammonites are rare, or in borehole chipping samples from which ammonites cannot be recovered.

LIAS GROUP

Rising sea level in late Triassic times flooded much of England and Wales, and marine conditions persisted throughout most of the Jurassic Period. In Early Jurassic times, the London Platform remained emergent or was a shoal area, but substantial thicknesses of mud-dominated sediments of the Lias Group accumulated in basins to the west and south of the platform and a thinner succession was deposited on the East Midlands Shelf to the north.

The Lias Group is best known from the coastal exposures of Dorset, Somerset, South Wales and Yorkshire. In our region, the area of outcrop is limited to that around Chipping Norton and Banbury, and in the Ouse valley near Stony Stratford in north Buckinghamshire (Figures 1 and 10). It also occurs extensively, at depth, beneath younger strata in the western and north-western parts of the region, and along its southern margin. In the Worcester Basin, the succession is very thick; 496 m were proved in the Stowell Park Borehole, just west of the region. Thick successions are also present in the Wessex Basin, reaching perhaps 400 m to the south of the region. The Lias Group thins towards the London Platform, where the sequence is condensed and, more importantly, the older beds are lost as they are progressively overlapped by younger beds which come to rest unconformably on the pre-Jurassic rocks of the platform. Thus the base of the Lias is highly diachronous (Table 3; Figure 10). The Lias is absent from the central and eastern parts of the region, which correspond with the centre of the London Platform.

The Lias Group is almost entirely of Early Jurassic age (Hettangian to Toarcian), although where the succession is fully developed, the basal beds are of late Triassic age (Rhaetian) (Table 3). Traditionally, the Lias has been subdivided into three parts, the Lower, Middle and Upper Lias. Although

Plate 2   Fossils from the Lias Group (all natural size, except 4 ($\times$ 0.5) and 8 ($\times$ 0.5)).

1   *Hildoceras bifrons* (Bruguière); Upper Lias
2   *Dactylioceras (Orthodactylites) semicelatum* (Simpson); Middle Lias: Marlstone Rock (Transition Bed)
3a–b   *Lobothyris punctata* (J Sowerby); Middle Lias
4   *Amaltheus margaritatus* de Montfort; Middle Lias
5a–b   *Tetrarhynchia tetrahedra* (J Sowerby); Middle Lias
6   *Pseudohastites* sp.; Lower Lias
7   *Pseudopecten equivalvis* (J Sowerby); Lower and Middle Lias
8a–b   *Microderoceras birchi* (J Sowerby); Lower Lias
9   *Protocardia truncata* (J de C Sowerby); Lower and Middle Lias
10   *Oxytoma inequivalve* (J Sowerby); Lower and Middle Lias
11   *Gryphaea arcuata* Lamarck; Lower Lias
12   *Plagiostoma giganteum* J Sowerby; Lower Lias

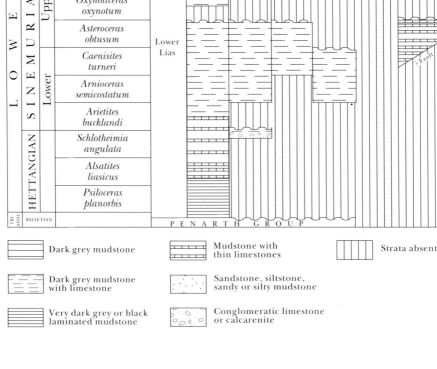

SYSTEM/SERIES	STAGE	SUBSTAGE	Ammonite biozone	TRADITIONAL SUBDIVISION	B O R E H O L E S				
					STOWELL PARK		STEEPLE ASTON	APLEY BARN WITNEY	WESTCOTT No.2	WARLINGHAM

Legend:

- Dark grey mudstone
- Dark grey mudstone with limestone
- Very dark grey or black laminated mudstone
- Mudstone with thin limestones
- Sandstone, siltstone, sandy or silty mudstone
- Conglomeratic limestone or calcarenite
- Strata absent

Table 3   Stratal subdivisions and main lithologies of the Lias Group.

these names are gradually being replaced by lithostratigraphically defined formational names, the new nomenclature has not yet been applied throughout the region, and so the traditional names are used here.

Lower Lias

The Lower Lias is Hettangian to early Pliensbachian in age. The succession is most complete in the Worcester Basin, where it attains its greatest thickness; it is 362 m thick in Stowell Park Borehole (Figure 10). The lower part of the sequence is a deeper-water equivalent of the well-known 'Blue Lias', seen for example at Lyme Regis in Dorset, in which limestones form a greater proportion of the succession. The rhythmic alternation of mudstone and limestone is probably related to periodic fluctuations in climate and water depth, accentuated by post-depositional diagenetic effects. The sequence passes up into grey mudstone, more or less calcareous and silty. The strata become generally more silty upwards and there is a lithological transition into the succeeding Middle Lias (Table 3).

Eastwards, on the northern flanks of the London Platform, the Lower Lias succession is much thinner. For example, Withycombe Farm Borehole, near Banbury (Figure 10), proved 154 m of mudstone with rare, thin limestones. Thin pebbly limestones at the base belong to the *Schlotheimia angulata* Zone; all earlier Jurassic beds, seen to the west in the Worcester Basin, are missing. Such basal conglomerates are common where the Lias laps onto the London Platform. They are diachronous, and in Westcott No. 2 and Chalgrove boreholes near Oxford, for example, similar beds belong to the much younger *Uptonia jamesoni* Zone (Table 3).

Warlingham Borehole (Figure 10), on the northern margin of the Wessex Basin, proved an attenuated Lower Lias succession, 98 m thick. The lower part of the succession is of 'Blue Lias' facies, comprising calcareous mudstone with many beds of silty limestone. The basal 10 m are of uncertain age, but the overlying beds (Table 3) range from the *Asteroceras obtusum* Zone upwards to the *Tragophylloceras ibex* Zone, and so are contemporaneous with mudstones in the Worcester Basin.

Middle Lias

The Middle Lias is late Pliensbachian in age (Table 3). In the Worcester and Wessex basins, it is 40 to 60 m in thickness, and at outcrop in north Oxfordshire, it is typically 20 to 30 m thick. It dies out towards the central parts of the London Platform. The deposits are generally coarser grained than those of the Lower Lias, having been laid down in shallower, higher- energy conditions.

The lower and thicker part of the succession belongs to the *Amaltheus margaritatus* Zone. It comprises pale grey, commonly slightly micaceous, silty mudstone, soft siltstone, and fine-grained sandstone; overall, the succession coarsens upwards. Sideritic ironstone nodules are common; they weather to brown limonite, commonly with a concentric laminar structure. Sporadic, thin, generally ferruginous and shelly limestones also occur.

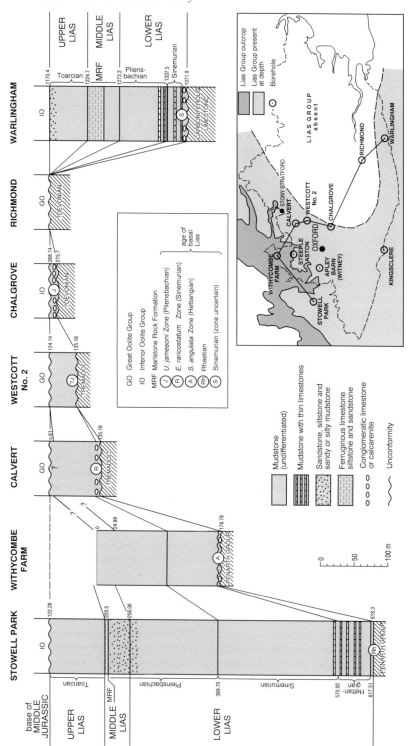

Figure 10   Stratigraphy and correlation of the Lias Group as proved in boreholes. Depths are measured from the ground surface.

The upper part of the Middle Lias comprises the **Marlstone Rock Formation** (Table 3), laid down in very shallow water. It consists of ferruginous limestone (typically with berthierine ooliths when fresh), sandstone and siltstone. In places, the base is conglomeratic indicating that localised erosion preceded deposition. Generally, the Marlstone Rock is about 1 to 3 m thick, but in contrast with other parts of the Lias, it is thickest on the shelf areas fringing the London Platform. The maximum for the region is about 7.5 m in the Banbury area, whereas Stowell Park Borehole in the Worcester Basin proved only 1.8 m (Figure 10). The iron content is also greatest in the shelf areas; near Banbury it may exceed 25 per cent. There, the Marlstone was formerly worked as an iron ore; it can still be seen in old quarries. The Marlstone is rich in brachiopods such as *Tetrarhynchia tetrahedra* (J Sowerby) and *Lobothyris punctata* (J Sowerby); bivalves, including *Protocardia, Pseudopecten* and *Oxytoma,* and belemnites are also locally common (Plate 2). Ammonites, mostly of the genus *Pleuroceras,* and including the zonal index *P. spinatum* (Brugière), are occasionally found, but are generally scarce in this shallow-water deposit. The very highest part of the Marlstone, termed the Transition Bed, locally yields early Toarcian faunas including *Dactylioceras (Orthodactylites) semicelatum* (Simpson) (Plate 2).

In Warlingham Borehole, the Middle Lias is 49 m thick (Figure 10). The upper part comprises nearly 20 m of calcareous sandstone, sandy limestone and ferruginous limestone, similar to the Marlstone elsewhere in the region. The precise age of these beds is uncertain, but they possibly extend down from the *spinatum* Zone into the *margaritatus* Zone (Table 3), which is proved in the underlying silty mudstones.

Upper Lias

The Upper Lias is Toarcian in age. Because of renewed transgression at this time, it is present over a larger area of the London Platform than the Middle Lias. It may originally have overlapped the Lower Lias, but it has been removed by later erosion in many areas. The thickest and most complete succession is in the Worcester Basin, where 98 m of mainly silty mudstone were proved in Stowell Park Borehole (Figure 10). In the shallower shelf area, represented at outcrop (Figure 1), only the oldest beds of the Upper Lias are preserved. They are up to 50 m thick, but thin towards the south-east. These beds are dominated by silty mudstone, but also contain thin beds of limestone and some thin, conglomeratic beds with phosphatised ooliths and reworked limestone concretions in a mudstone matrix. The basal part, known as the **Fish Beds**, is up to 2 m thick. It comprises olive-grey, bituminous, laminated mudstones alternating with pale, greenish grey, calcareous mudstones and limestones. The Fish Beds contain a rich ammonite fauna, indicating the early part of the *Harpoceras falciferum* Zone; bivalves, small brachiopods and the remains of fish and rare insects also occur. The overlying **Cephalopod Limestones** consists of 1 to 2 m of calcareous mudstone, marl and micritic limestone, with concentrations of small phosphatic ooliths at several horizons. The member takes its name from its rich ammonite fauna, which indicates the *falciferum* Zone and the early part of the *Hildoceras bifrons* Zone (Plate 2). It also contains bivalves, crinoids and belemnites. The overlying beds, making up the greater part of the Upper Lias, are grey mudstone, with sporadic limestone nodules including ferruginous and phosphatic types. These beds yield some bivalves (notably *Dacryomya ovum* (J de C Sowerby)), but are generally poorly fossiliferous. In Warlingham Borehole, the Upper Lias is 54 m thick (Figure 10), and consists largely of beds of this type.

A drop in sea level in Late Toarcian times led to erosion on the London Platform, which was stripped of its youngest Upper Lias sediments; no beds younger than the *bifrons* Zone are known from boreholes on, or close to, the London Platform (Table 3). The highest parts of the preserved Upper Lias are commonly altered to pale greenish grey, locally variegated, seatearth mudstones, due to long exposure prior to burial in Mid Jurassic times. Detritus from the platform accumulated in the Worcester and Wessex basins, where the youngest Upper Lias beds comprise sands and silts, including the Cotteswold Sands (Table 3). In Warlingham Borehole, the uppermost 8 m of the Upper Lias comprises silty mudstone with some layers of limonitic, oolitic ironstone, which may equate with late Toarcian ironstones known from boreholes in the Weald.

4 Jurassic: Inferior Oolite and Great Oolite groups

The Inferior Oolite and Great Oolite groups (Tables 2 and 4), of Mid Jurassic age, are composed dominantly of limestones, which give rise to broad uplands dissected by steep-sided valleys. Best developed in the Cotswold Hills, these strata have a limited outcrop in north Oxfordshire and Buckinghamshire (Figures 1 and 13). They persist down-dip below younger beds, until they pinch out against the London Platform. They are thus absent from much of the eastern part of the region, but they occur at depth in the south, on the margins of the Wessex Basin, where they have been proved in boreholes such as those at Warlingham, and at Humbly Grove, near Basingstoke (Figure 11).

The stratigraphy of the Inferior Oolite and Great Oolite is complicated by rapid variations in lithology and thickness, which are related to changing environments of deposition across the region. Sea level was generally lower than in the Early Jurassic, so that the emergent areas increased northwards from the London Platform onto the East Midlands Shelf. In the northern part of the region, therefore, much of the succession is of nearshore and nonmarine facies, similar to those which are more fully developed in the East Midlands and Yorkshire. In the west and south of the region, the margins of the London Platform were covered by a shallow sea, in which carbonate-dominated sediments were deposited. The adjoining Worcester and Wessex basins (Figure 8), where the thickest successions occur, were areas of more open sea, and mud deposition predominated at times. However, subsidence was much diminished compared with that of the Early Jurassic, and shallow-water, carbonate deposition extended far into the basins at times. Thickness changes are particularly marked in the lower part of the Inferior Oolite Group, when traced eastwards from the Worcester Basin onto the London Platform. These thickness changes have traditionally been ascribed to a locus of relative uplift, the 'Vale of Moreton Axis' (or 'Swell'), which corresponds with the western edge of the London Platform (Figures 12 and 13). The effects of the Moreton Axis on thickness were greatly diminished during the Bathonian, when the Great Oolite Group was deposited.

INFERIOR OOLITE GROUP

At outcrop within the region, the Inferior Oolite, succession is incomplete, representing only a small part of the succession developed near Cheltenham, to the west. In particular, the middle part of the succession is missing, and a major non-sequence separates the lower and upper parts (Table 4).

In the Lower Inferior Oolite, the **Scissum Beds** comprise up to 3 m of pale grey sandy limestone; there is generally a thin bed with small phosphatic

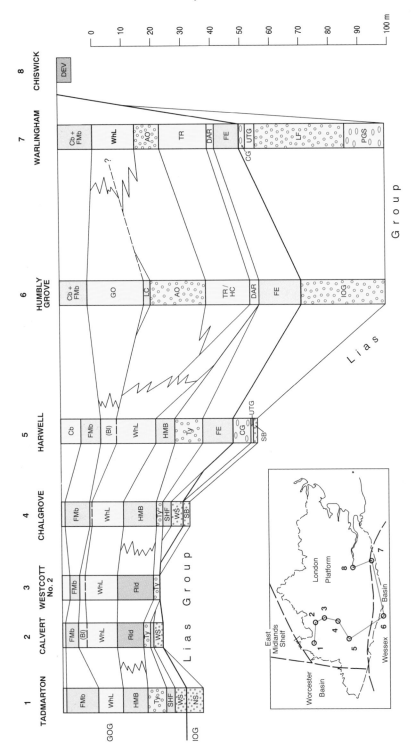

pebbles at the base. The Scissum Beds occur throughout the western part of the region but, towards the north-east, in Oxfordshire, they are replaced by the **Northampton Sand**, which comprises up to 12 m of sideritic, sandy, bio-turbated, shell-fragmental and oolitic limestones with thin sideritic mudstones; shelly beds occur at some horizons. The formation was formerly exploited as an iron ore in the Wellingborough area, just north of the region. The Scissum Beds and Northampton Sand were deposited in shallow marine waters. Iron compounds were probably carried into the depositional area of the Northampton Sand by rivers draining nearby land, where lateritic soils were developed. East of Brackley, the Northampton Sand is absent, and the Inferior Oolite Group is represented only by the largely nonmarine **Grantham Formation**, which comprises pale grey sands, silts and clays, with common rootlet beds.

Younger strata of the Lower Inferior Oolite have been proved at depth to the west of the Moreton Axis; the sequence proved by a borehole near Cirencester is 35 m thick (Figure 12). The succession, comprising the **Pea Grit 'Series'**, **Lower Freestone**, **Oolite Marl** and **Upper Freestone**, is dominated by oolitic limestone, indicating deposition in a shallow, current-swept shelf sea. By contrast, the Pea Grit, within the upper part of the Pea Grit 'Series', is characterised by oncoliths, large ovoid grains formed by algal overgrowth on a shell-fragment nucleus in low-energy conditions. Similarly, the marls and carbonate mudstones which form a major part of the Oolite Marl, suggest quiet-water, lagoonal conditions. Lower Inferior Oolite is also known in the southern part of the region, for example in the Warlingham Borehole, where the strata are some 44 m thick (Figure 11).

Within much of the London and Thames Valley region, widespread erosion of the earlier Inferior Oolite strata removed the succession from most areas. The Middle Inferior Oolite is a thin but complex succession with many breaks, and is preserved only to the west of the Moreton Axis. A renewed transgression in Late Bajocian times is marked by the **Upper Trigonia Grit** (Table 4), the basal unit of the Upper Inferior Oolite. It comprises up to 4 m of hard, very shelly limestone, locally with a basal conglomeratic bed, and overlies an eroded and bored surface of gently folded Lower Inferior Oolite (Figure 12).

The succeeding **Clypeus Grit**, the topmost unit of the Inferior Oolite, consists of 8 to 15 m of buff-weathering, shelly, oolitic and pisolitic lime-stones. Generally, it has a fine-grained micrite matrix, indicating low-energy conditions; the ooliths and pisoliths were probably swept in from nearby shoals. East of Fairford (Figure 13), the lower part of the Clypeus Grit is par-

Figure 11 Stratigraphy and correlation of the Inferior and Great Oolite groups as proved in boreholes, illustrating attenuation of the succession over the London Platform.

Great Oolite Group (GOG): AO, Athelstan Oolite; Bl, Bladon Member/Signet Member; Cb, Cornbrash; DAR, Dodington Ash Rock; FE, Fuller's Earth; FMb Forest Marble; GO, Great Oolite Formation; HC Hawkesbury Clay; HMB, Hampen Formation; LC, Lansdown Clay; Rld, Rutland Formation; SHF, Sharp's Hill Formation; TR, Tresham Rock; Ty, Taynton Limestone; WhL, White Limestone; WS, White Sands. Inferior Oolite Group (IOG): CG, Clypeus Grit; LF, Lower Freestone; NS, Northampton Sand; PGS, Pea Grit 'Series'; SB, Scissum Beds; UTG, Upper Trigonia Grit, DEV, Devonian.

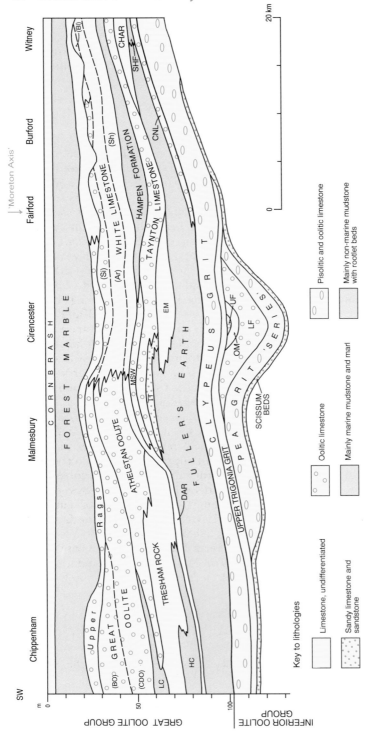

ticularly coarsely pisolitic, marly and is poorly sorted. A marginal, sandy, ironshot facies of this lower unit occurs to the east of Witney. The Clypeus Grit is richly fossiliferous and contains abundant brachiopods such as *Stiphrothyris tumida* (Davidson), echinoids including *Clypeus ploti* Salter, and bivalves.

GREAT OOLITE GROUP

Marked regional changes in facies and thickness characterise much of the Great Oolite Group. The group thins towards the north-east along the outcrop, from about 60m in Wiltshire to about 20 m in Bedfordshire (Figures 12 and 13). In the south Cotswolds, between Chippenham and Cirencester, a profusion of local formational names reflects rapid lateral and vertical lithological variations (Table 4). In this area, there is an interdigitation between deeper-water, argillaceous formations, such as the Fuller's Earth, more typically developed in the Wessex Basin, and shallow-water carbonates which were deposited around the margins of the London Platform. Carbonate deposition progressively invaded the basinal area, so that the bases of limestone formations are commonly mildly diachronous, becoming younger to the south-west. Another facies change occurs in the central and north-eastern part of the outcrop, where much of the marine succession passes gradually into beds which were laid down in coastal swamps and lagoons on the northern margin of the London Platform. In certain parts of the sequence, these effects can be seen as far west as Witney and, north-east of Brackley (Figure 13), most of the lower part of the Great Oolite Group is represented by nonmarine facies, the Rutland Formation.

Detailed correlation between the different facies is hindered by the rarity of ammonites and other age-diagnostic fossils; the zonation shown in Table 4 is based on only a few specimens. However, depositional breaks, probably related to changes in sea-level and sediment supply, have been recognised throughout the region, and these are of great value in temporal correlation. In the basinal succession, they are marked by burrowed horizons: on the carbonate shelf, by bored and oyster-encrusted hardground surfaces, erosional contacts and conglomeratic horizons: in the nonmarine facies, by beds with rootlets and structures indicating subaerial emergence.

In the west of the region, the **Fuller's Earth Formation**, at the base of the Great Oolite Group, comprises up to 25 m of mudstone with thin, muddy limestones and shell beds; persistent shell beds containing an abundance of

Figure 12 Diagrammatic section showing lateral variation in the Inferior and Great Oolite groups: Chippenham to Witney (see Figure 13 for locality map).

Great Oolite Group: Ar, Ardley Member; Bl, Bladon Member; BO, Bath Oolite; CDO, Combe Down Oolite; CHAR, Charlbury Formation; CNL, Chipping Norton Limestone; DAR, Dodington Ash Rock; HC, Hawkesbury Clay; LC, Lansdown Clay; MSW, Minchinhampton Shelly beds and Weatherstones; Sh, Shipton Member; Si, Signet Member; SHF, Sharps Hill Formation; TT, Througham Tilestones.

Inferior Oolite Group: LF, Lower Freestone; OM, Oolite Marl; UF, Upper Freestone.

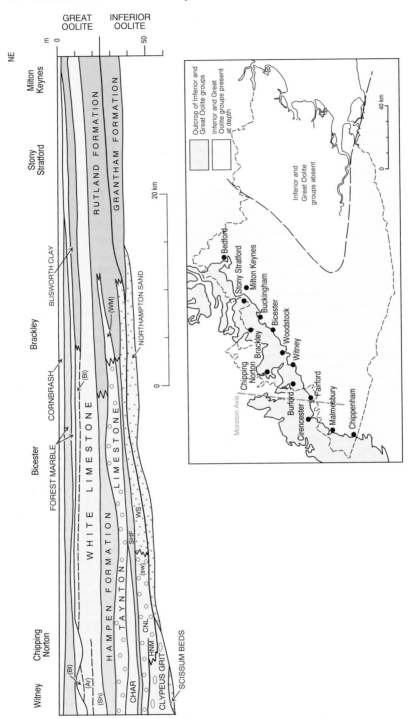

the small oyster *Praeexogyra acuminata* (J Sowerby) (Plate 3:11), are valuable markers for correlation.

North-eastwards, the Fuller's Earth thins, due to lateral passage of the lower and upper parts into limestone facies. At Burford, the basal part is replaced by the **Chipping Norton Limestone Formation**, comprising fawn, well-sorted oolites with sporadic shelly beds (Plate 4) and, locally, a thin bed of mudstone (Roundhill Clay Member) at its base. In the Chipping Norton area, this formation is up to 11 m thick; its lower part comprises sandy limestones known as the Hook Norton Member, which is probably equivalent to the youngest part of the Clypeus Grit (Inferior Oolite Group) farther west (Table 4). The Chipping Norton Limestone becomes increasingly sandy and less oolitic eastwards, and passes into the **Swerford Member**. The **White Sands**, which appear near Steeple Aston, comprise white, pale grey and brown, quartz sands with sporadic, thin, mudstone beds, containing plant debris. Palynological evidence suggests that the White Sands equate with the Chipping Norton Limestone and pass north-eastward into the lowest part (Stamford Member) of the Rutland Formation (Figure 13), although they have been included in the Grantham Formation (Inferior Oolite Group) by some workers.

In north Oxfordshire, the Fuller's Earth above the Chipping Norton Limestone passes eastwards into the **Sharp's Hill Formation**, which comprises up to 3 m of green to dark grey mudstone interbedded with thin shelly limestones, marls, siltstones and, locally, sandstones (Plate 4). Rootlet beds, seatearths and carbonaceous plant debris are common. The formation contains a diverse molluscan fauna including marine forms such as the oyster *Praeexogyra hebridica* (Forbes) (Plate 3:9), corals and brachiopods, brackish-water forms including the bivalves *Cuspidaria ibbetsoni* (Morris) and *Placunopsis socialis* Morris & Lycett, and some freshwater forms such as the gastropod *Viviparus langtonensis* (Hudleston).

North-eastwards from Cirencester, the uppermost beds of the Fuller's Earth pass laterally into marly, oolitic and sandy limestone and mudstone. Fissile sandy limestone (**Eyford Member**) at this horizon was formerly worked as 'Cotswold Slates' for roofing, near Stow-on-the-Wold. These beds are absent over the Moreton Axis, where they are overstepped by the Taynton Limestone Formation (see below). Equivalents reappear east of Burford, where they are known as the **Charlbury Formation**, which comprises shell-fragmental and shelly, marly limestones interbedded with shelly marls (Plate 4). The beds contain a variety of marine bivalves and species of the brachiopods *Epithyris* and *Kallirhynchia*.

The overlying **Taynton Limestone Formation** is characterised by cross-bedded, shell-fragmental oolites. Locally, it is up to 10 m thick, and was once extensively quarried for building stone. Near Cirencester, the Taynton Limestone passes

Figure 13 Diagrammatic section showing lateral variation in the Inferior and Great Oolite groups: Witney to Milton Keynes (see Figure 12 for key to ornament).

Great Oolite Group: Ar, Ardley Member; Bl, Bladon Member; CHAR, Charlbury Formation; CNL, Chipping Norton Limestone; EM, Eyford Member; HNM, Hook Norton Member; Sh, Shipton Member; SHF, Sharps Hill Formation; SW, Swerford Member; WM, Wellingborough Member; WS, White Sands.

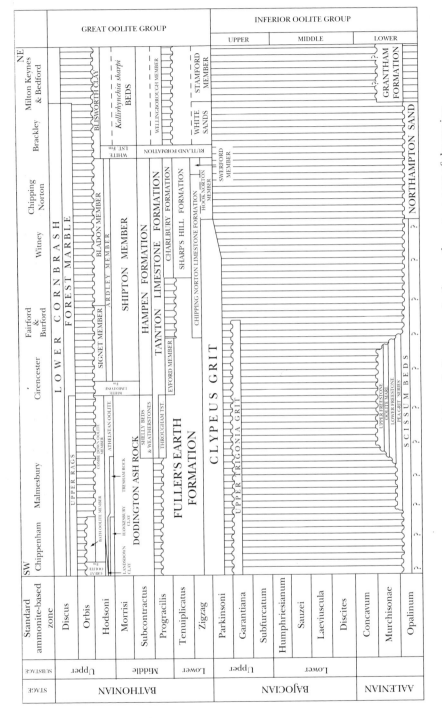

Table 4   Main stratal subdivisions of the Inferior and Great Oolite groups in the north-western part of the region.

westwards into the **Througham Tilestone Formation**, which comprises up to 6 m of fissile, thinly bedded, sandy limestones interbedded with sandy mudstones, similar to the 'Cotswold Slates'. At Stonesfield, near Woodstock in Oxfordshire, similar, but impersistent, beds of sandy 'tilestone' with oolitic partings, are developed at three levels within the Taynton Limestone. These beds, known as **Stonesfield Slate**, were once mined for roofing stone. They contain an indigenous marine fauna with bivalves such as *Trigonia impressa* J Sowerby, gastropods, rhynchonellid brachiopods and fish, but are especially noted for the remains of dinosaurs, early mammals, insects and a variety of plants. These were washed into the sea from nearby land on the London Platform.

The Taynton Limestone is overlain by the **Hampen Formation**, which comprises up to 10 m of grey and greenish grey mudstone, siltstone and marl, with variously micritic, sandy, shell-fragmental and shelly limestones, and fine-grained oolites. The beds yield a diverse fauna including the brachiopods *Kallirhynchia concinna* (J Sowerby) and *Epithyris bathonica* S S Buckman, and numerous bivalves. Oyster shell beds containing abundant *P. hebridica* are common east of Burford. In the Bicester area, clays and silts with rootlet beds, brackish-water bivalves such as *Corbula* and *Cuspidaria*, freshwater ostracods, and land-derived dinosaur (*Cetiosaurus*) bones indicate a coastal marsh environment. West of Burford, where fully marine conditions prevailed, limestones dominate, and beyond Cirencester, the formation passes into the '**Minchinhampton Shelly Beds and Weatherstones**', which comprise shelly oolites and hard, shell-fragmental, oolitic limestones. Southwest of Malmesbury, these are thought to pass into the lower part of the **Dodington Ash Rock**, which consists of up to 5 m of silty and micritic limestones containing scattered shell detritus, algal-coated oncoliths and ferruginous grains. This succession contains many non-sequences marked by bored and eroded surfaces.

In the western part of the region, the succeeding **Hawkesbury Clay** comprises up to 8 m of mudstone with a few thin limestones. It is overlain by, and passes laterally into the **Tresham Rock**, composed of fine-grained, silty, commonly bioturbated limestones, up to 16m thick. North-eastward, these two units are replaced by shell-detrital, oolitic limestones known as the **Athelstan Oolite**, which is up to 20 m in thickness. Its topmost bed is commonly a bored or oyster-encrusted hardground. The overlying **Lansdown Clay** represents the feather-edge of the Upper Fuller's Earth of the Wessex Basin, where virtually the whole of the Great Oolite Group is represented by mudstones.

The lower part of the succeeding **Great Oolite Formation** (from which the group takes its name) is the Combe Down Oolite Member. This is characterised by creamy grey and yellow, shell-detrital oolites, less well sorted than those of the Athelstan Oolite. Like the latter, the uppermost bed of the Combe Down Oolite is a bored hardground. The overlying Bath Oolite Member consists of cream, fine and well-sorted oolitic freestones which were once extensively mined for building stone near Bath.

Near Cirencester, the upper part of the Dodington Ash Rock, the Athelstan Oolite and the Combe Down Oolite, merge to form the **White Limestone Formation**, which extends north-eastwards through Oxfordshire, Buckinghamshire and into Bedfordshire. The formation is typically some 20 m thick. It is dominated by pale cream and white, micritic or very finely detrital, bio-

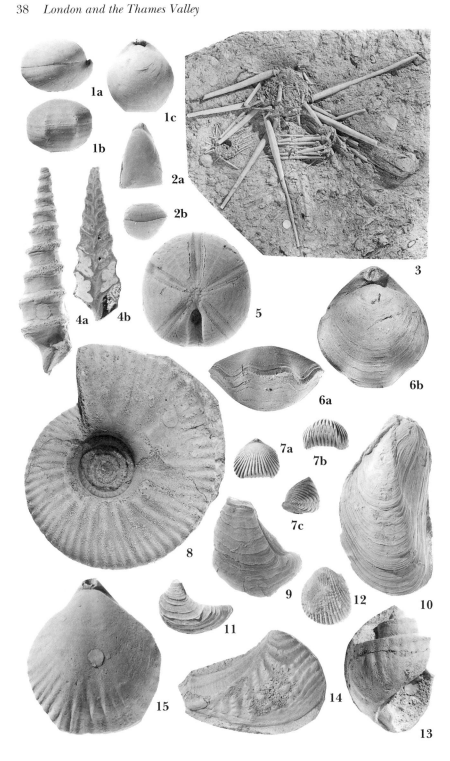

Plate 3 Fossils from the Inferior Oolite and Great Oolite groups (all natural size except 3 ($\times 0.5$)).

1a–c *Obovothyris magnobovata* S S Buckman; Great Oolite Group: Cornbrash
2a–b *Digonella digona* (J Sowerby); Great Oolite Group: Forest Marble
3 *Acrosalenia hemicidaroides* Wright; Great Oolite Group
4a–b *Cossmannea (Eunerinea) eudesi* Morris & Lycett; Great Oolite Group
5 *Nucleolites orbicularis* (Phillips); Great Oolite Group: Cornbrash
6a–b *Epithyris oxonica* Arkell; Great Oolite Group: White Limestone
7a–c *Rhynchonelloidella smithi* (Davidson); Great Oolite Group: Fuller's Earth
8 *Wagnericeras suspensum* (S S Buckman); Great Oolite Group: Dodington Ash Rock
9 *Praeexogyra [Liostrea] hebridica* (Forbes); Great Oolite Group: Fuller's Earth
10 *Modiolus imbricatus* (J Sowerby); Great Oolite Group
11 *Praeexogyra [Liostrea] acuminata* (J Sowerby); Great Oolite Group: Fuller's Earth
12 *Meleagrinella echinata* (Wm Smith); Great Oolite Group
13 *Ampullospira sharpei* (Morris & Lycett); Great Oolite Group: White Limestone
14 *Vaugonia angulata* (J de C Sowerby); Great Oolite Group: Cornbrash
15 *Plectothyris polyplectus* (S S Buckman); Inferior Oolite Group

Plate 4 Town Quarry, Charlbury, Oxfordshire. The lower part of the quarry is excavated in Chipping Norton Limestone, locally the basal unit of the Great Oolite Group. This is overlain by dark grey clays of the Sharp's Hill Formation, which is in turn succeeded by the buff marls and marly limestones of the Charlbury Formation, and the paler Taynton Limestone Formation above (A15217). B Boneham.

turbated, variably peloidal limestone, with sporadic marl or clay beds. The fauna is dominated by bivalves and brachiopods such as *Epithyris oxonica* Arkell; high-spired gastropods including *Aphanoptyxis* and *Cossmannea* also occur at certain horizons (Plate 3). Over much of the region, the formation is divisible into three members (Table 4), namely the Shipton, Ardley and Bladon members.

The Shipton Member generally contains a higher proportion of terrigenous clay than the overlying strata. Its top is marked by the *Aphanoptyxis excavata* Bed which is locally capped by a hardground. Near Brackley, this bed is replaced by a rootlet bed indicating emergent conditions. The succeeding Ardley Member includes a widespread sandy limestone ('Roach Bed') near the base, and cross-bedded, shell-detrital, oolitic limestone is present locally, particularly west of Witney. The *Aphanoptyxis bladonensis* Bed at the top of the member is generally capped by a bored hardground surface. At some localities in the Bicester area, this bed contains algal laminae and other structures indicating periodic emergence. The lower part of the succeeding Bladon Member is the Fimbriata-Waltoni Bed, named from the bivalves *Eomiodon fimbriata* (Lycett) and *Bakevellia waltoni* (Lycett). It comprises green and grey mudstones, with some marls and marly limestones, and commonly contains rootlets and logs of driftwood, indicating a coastal marsh environment. Remains of dinosaurs such as *Cetiosaurus* have been found at several localities near Oxford. The overlying Upper Epithyris Bed consists most typically of micritic limestones, locally characterised by an abundance of the brachiopod *Epithyris* and branching corals. Elsewhere, it includes marly and shell-detrital limestones, commonly with abundant *Modiolus* (Plate 3:10). At Burford, the Bladon Member passes westwards into the Signet Member, which comprises rubbly, argillaceous sandy and micritic limestones, oolitic limestones and clays. The Fairford Coral Bed is developed locally at its top; this contains well-preserved compound corals, including *Isastraea* and *Thamnasteria*.

In the Brackley–Bedford district, the White Limestone was formerly known as the Blisworth Limestone. It has a larger component of clastic sediment than farther west, and rootlet horizons also occur; these indicate marshy or emergent conditions. The basal 2 m or so are characterised by the rhynchonellid *Kallirhynchia sharpi* Muir-Wood. Higher in the sequence, the occurrence of *Digonella digonoides* (S S Buckman) suggests correlation with the Ardley Member. The overlying **Blisworth Clay** consists of 4 to 6 m of green, grey and purple-mottled, seatearth mudstones, with some beds of shelly mudstone and limestone. Rootlet beds, and a mixed fauna with marine, brackish and freshwater elements, reflect a marginal environment, similar to that in which the Fimbriata-Waltoni Bed was deposited. The Blisworth Clay has traditionally been correlated with the Forest Marble of districts to the south-west. However, it is now thought that the Blisworth Clay is probably the lateral equivalent of the Bladon Member of the White Limestone Formation (Table 4).

In this northern part of the region, the succession in the lower part of the Great Oolite Group, including the White Sands, the Sharp's Hill, Taynton Limestone and Hampen formations, lose their identity where they pass into a nonmarine facies. North-eastwards from Brackley, this part of the Great Oolite Group is classified as the **Rutland Formation**, which is up to 20 m thick. The Stamford Member at the base, comprises commonly white sands and silts, and dark, varicoloured clays and mudstones with some rootlets. The overlying strata consist of mudstone, clay and silt, with sporadic thin limestones and marls in a sequence of shallowing-upwards rhythms. Each rhythm typically commences with a laminated shelly mudstone, and terminates with a rootlet bed. Bivalves are common in the mudstones; at some horizons, forms such as *Cuspidaria bathonica* Cox & Arkell and *Placunopsis socialis* Morris & Lycett indicate brackish water conditions. The Wellingborough Member, in the middle of the formation, comprises up to 6m of alternating marls and micritic limestones, in parts sandy or silty. It contains a predominantly marine fauna, and is probably equivalent to the Taynton Limestone Formation farther south-west.

Throughout the region, a period of erosion followed the deposition of the Great Oolite Formation and its equivalents (Table 4). The succeeding **Forest Marble Formation** marked a return to a more uniform, shallow shelf sea. The earliest deposits in the western part of the region, known as the **Upper Rags** (or Acton Turville Beds in the Malmesbury area), comprise up to 8 m of shell-fragmental, cross-bedded oolitic limestones, formed in current-swept waters. Patch coral reefs occur near the base. Although the Upper Rags are not recognised as a discrete member north-east of Fairford, limestones continue to dominate the lower part of the Forest Marble succession. Flaggy, shell-fragmental, oyster-rich limestones are particularly prominent, locally infilling channels which cut down several metres into the underlying beds. The upper part of the Forest Marble Formation is dominated by greenish grey mudstone, up to 25 m thick in the west. It contains lenticles and burrow-fills of sandy limestone, and larger, channel-filling bodies of sandy limestone and calcareous sandstone also occur, reflecting sporadic increases in current activity. The Forest Marble thins to the north-east, and beyond Bicester, where it overlies Blisworth Clay, it is generally only about 5m thick. There, the Forest Marble is almost entirely composed of limestones; the mudstones of the upper part appear to have been removed by erosion prior to deposition of the overlying Cornbrash and, beyond Milton Keynes, the Forest Marble is cut out entirely, so that the Cornbrash rests on the Blisworth Clay (Figure 13).

The **Cornbrash Formation** is the youngest of the Great Oolite Group. It was deposited over much of southern England during a widespread transgression, and crops out across the region from Chippenham to Bedford (Figures 12 and 13). Generally about 3 to 5 m thick, it consists mainly of fine-grained, shell-fragmental limestone with thin clays and marls. It commonly contains marly burrow-fills and shows much evidence of reworking in the form of pebble beds. It is a massive, bluish grey limestone, but on weathering it yields a brown, rubbly brash. The Lower Cornbrash, of Bathonian age, rests abruptly, and generally with evidence of slight erosion, upon the underlying beds. Typically, it contains abundant brachiopods, *Cererithyris intermedia* (J Sowerby) at the base, and *Ornithella obovata* (J Sowerby) above, associated with echinoids, bivalves and serpulids. The Upper Cornbrash is Callovian in age, and is lithologically similar. The diverse fauna includes the zonal ammonite *Macrocephalites*, and brachiopods *Microthyridina siddingtonensis* (Walker) at the base and *M. lagenalis* (Schlotheim) above. In the south-west in Wiltshire and south Oxfordshire, both subdivisions are present, although the Upper Cornbrash is generally very thin, and may be absent east of Woodstock.

North-eastwards, both divisions are present in the Buckingham, Milton Keynes and Bedford areas.

In the subsurface, along the southern margin of the region, the Great Oolite Group is present in Humbly Grove and Warlingham boreholes (Figure 11). The succession is similar to that in the Cotswolds of Gloucestershire. South of London, the Great Oolite Group oversteps the Inferior Oolite and Lias to rest directly upon Devonian strata in boreholes at Streatham and Richmond. The original extent of the Great Oolite on the London Platform is unknown, but it has undoubtedly been stripped from many areas by later, mainly early Cretaceous, erosion.

5   Jurassic: Ancholme and Corallian groups, Portland and Purbeck formations

The marine transgression, which began with the Cornbrash in latest Bathonian times, continued into the Callovian, and deepening waters encroached farther onto the London Platform than at any previous time in the Mesozoic. The mud-dominated sediments deposited comprise the Ancholme Group, of late Mid and Late Jurassic age (Table 2). Much of the constituent clay material was probably derived from the remaining land areas of the London Platform. At times, the platform may have been entirely submerged, but it remained an area of reduced subsidence. The outcrop of the Ancholme Group forms a belt of low-lying country to the south-east of the Cotswolds (Figures 1 and 3). The succession preserved in the region is much thinner than in the Wessex Basin to the south (Figure 2). In the west of the region, a marked local thickening of the lowest part of the Ancholme Group appears to be related to the eastern margin of the Worcester Basin.

In Late Oxfordian times, there was a short-lived change to shallower, higher-energy conditions. This was, perhaps, accompanied by a change to a warmer and drier climate, with an associated reduction in the amount of clastic material carried into the seas. Local coral growth, and carbonate deposition occurred on the margins of the London Platform. These sediments constitute the Corallian Group, which crops out between Calne and Oxford where it intercalates with the mudstone of the Ancholme Group. In the following account, the Corallian Group is discussed after the Ancholme Group.

Mud deposition continued in Kimmeridgian times but, due to falling sea level, was replaced by shallow-water sedimentation in the succeeding Port-landian. The Portland Formation comprises marine sandstones and carbonates, and, as sea level continued to fall, the youngest part of the Jurassic sequence, the Purbeck Formation, was deposited in shallow-marine, inter-tidal, coastal and lagoonal conditions.

ANCHOLME GROUP

The basal unit of the Ancholme Group (Table 5) is the **Kellaways Formation**, which crops out across the north-west of the region between Chippenham and Bedford (Figure 14). In the north-eastern half of the outcrop, it is typically 5m to 6m thick. The formation persists south-eastwards, down-dip, and is also present along the southern margin of the region, where boreholes at Kingsclere and Warlingham have proved thicknesses of 9m and 5m respectively. In the south-west of the region, the thickness of the formation is much greater, and up to 25m are recorded in boreholes in Wiltshire (Figure 15).

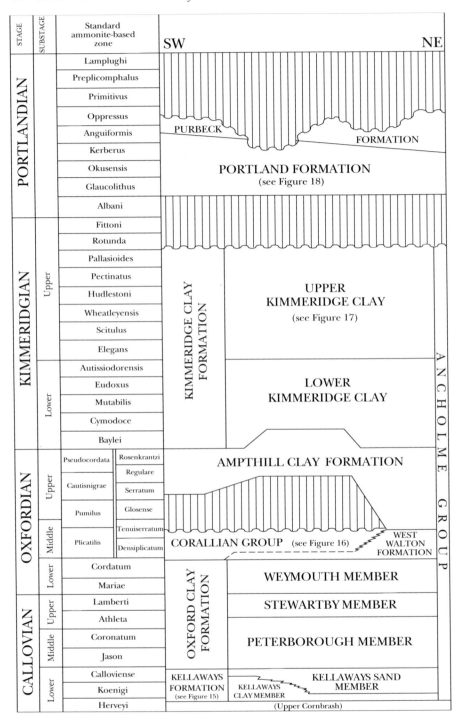

Table 5   Main stratal subdivisions of the youngest Jurassic rocks of the region.

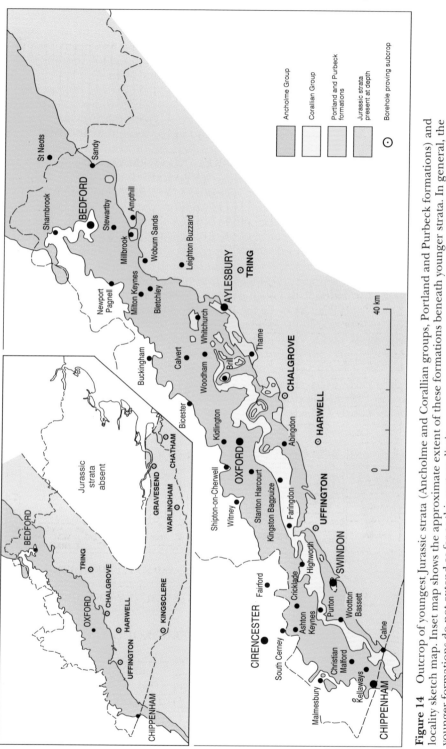

Figure 14 Outcrop of youngest Jurassic strata (Ancholme and Corallian groups, Portland and Purbeck formations) and locality sketch map. Inset map shows the approximate extent of these formations beneath younger strata. In general, the younger formations do not extend as far as this eastern limit.

Much of this thickening occurs in the neighbourhood of Cricklade, where boreholes indicate a marked westward increase from 12 m to over 20 m within a distance of a few kilometres. The narrow zone in which the thickening takes place corresponds with the southward extension of the Moreton Axis, which marks the eastern margin of the Worcester Basin.

The formation takes its name from the locality of Kellaways, on the River Avon near Chippenham, which, in latinised form, also gives its name to the Callovian Stage. Cored boreholes nearby at West Tytherton provide type or reference sections for both the formation and its constituent members.

The formation is divisible into two members, traditionally known as the Kellaways Clay and overlying Kellaways Sand. The **Kellaways Clay Member** is itself divisible into two. The thinner, lower unit is widespread, and is developed throughout most of the region (Figure 15). It has recently been named separately as the 'Cayton Clay Formation'. It is generally about 3m thick, and consists of dark grey, smooth-textured, shaly or silty mudstone with phosphatic nodules. It is usually poorly fossiliferous with bivalves, including *Corbulomima*, *Modiolus* and nuculoids, serpulids and procerithiid gastropods. Species of the ammonite *Macrocephalites* indicate the youngest subzone of the Herveyi Zone. The upper, and thicker, part of the Kellaways Clay is responsible for the formational thickening in the west, and indicates a relatively sudden and short-lived episode of subsidence in the Worcester Basin. It consists of pale to medium grey, sandy or silty mudstone with thin muddy sandstone beds, and cementstone nodules including large septaria. Molluscan faunas, particularly bivalves and ammonites, are relatively abundant. Well-preserved ammonites from the Wiltshire type area are present in nearly every major fossil collection in Britain, as well as many elsewhere in Europe. They include species of the genera *Kepplerites*, *Proplanulites*, *Cadoceras* and *Chamoussetia*, indicative of the Koenigi Zone.

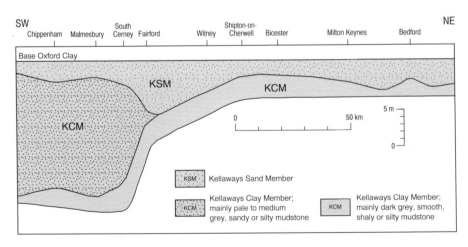

Figure 15   Thickness variation in the Kellaways Formation; Chippenham to Bedford. Based on Page (1989, fig. 3) with modifications from borehole and mapping evidence in the Witney–Fairford area.

In the west, in Wiltshire, the **Kellaways Sand Member** is developed mainly as calcareous sandstone, with richly fossiliferous concretions, and was formerly known as 'Kellaways Rock'. It is exposed in the banks of the River Avon at Kellaways. To the north-east, softer, less fossiliferous, poorly cemented or uncemented sands are more typical. These have been exposed, from time to time, in the floors of brickpits working the Oxford Clay in Buckinghamshire and Bedfordshire. Oysters, belemnites and wood fragments are characteristic fossils of this member. In the Wiltshire type area, ammonite species, in particular those of *Sigaloceras* (Plate 5:7) and *Proplanulites*, indicate the Calloviense Zone. However, farther north, the member also includes beds of the preceding Koenigi Zone, which correlate with the thick Kellaways Clay Member of the south-west (Table 5).

The **Oxford Clay Formation** extends in a broad belt through the city of Oxford, which gives its name to the formation. The clay was formerly worked in a number of brickpits and these, together with temporary exposures and cored boreholes, provide a detailed knowledge of the formation. Brick pits at Purton in Wiltshire (Plate 6), Woodham, Calvert and Bletchley in Buckinghamshire and Stewartby near Bedford, have been particularly important in establishing the subdivisions of the formation, and the standard ammonite-based zonation of the Callovian and Oxfordian stages (Table 5). Christian Malford in Wiltshire (Figure 14), where exposures were recorded and fossils collected during construction of the Great Western Railway in the nineteenth century, is another famous Oxford Clay locality within the region. Only the pits at Stewartby remain active.

In the Oxford area and to the north-east, the formation is between 65m and 75m thick. South-westwards from Oxford into the area of the Worcester Basin, the thickness almost certainly increases, and may be up to twice that in the north-east of the region. The Oxford Clay extends south-eastwards, down-dip, beneath younger strata, but its extent over the London Platform is imprecisely known. It also extends along the southern margin of the region, but published thicknesses of 96 m at Kingsclere and 97 m at Warlingham undoubtedly represent both the Oxford Clay and overlying West Walton Formation. The Oxford Clay has also been proved beneath Cretaceous strata in the Gravesend and Chatham area in the east of the region.

The formation is divided into three members (Table 5). The oldest, the **Peterborough Member** (formerly known as the Lower Oxford Clay), is the best known because of extensive working by the London Brick Company in Buckinghamshire and Bedfordshire. It comprises brownish grey, fissile, organic-rich ('bituminous'), shelly mudstone, with a fauna dominated by aragonitic ammonites (in particular *Kosmoceras* which is used as the basis of the standard zonation) and bivalves. The latter include *Meleagrinella* (Plate 5:2) and nuculaceans, both of which occur abundantly in virtually monospecific shell beds. Subordinate, pale to medium grey, blocky mudstone and several bands of cementstone nodules also occur. The most important and widespread marker horizons are the Comptoni Bed and overlying Acutistriatum Band. Named respectively after the ammonites *Binatisphinctes comptoni* (Pratt) (Plate 5:1) and *Kosmoceras acutistriatum* (S S Buckman), both horizons may contain cementstone nodules. The Acutistriatum Band is a hard, calcareous, generally sparsely shelly, shaly mudstone about 0.3 m thick, which marks the base of the Athleta Zone (Table 5). The Comptoni Bed is a thin, pyritised

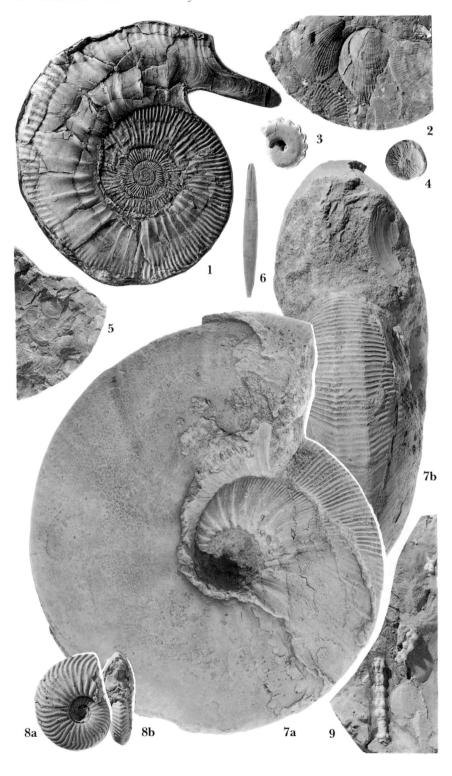

Plate 5 Fossils from the Kellaways and Oxford Clay formations (all natural size).

1   *Binatisphinctes comptoni* (Pratt); Oxford Clay: Peterborough Member
2   *Meleagrinella braamburiensis* (Phillips); Kellaways and Oxford Clay formations
3   *Creniceras rengerri* (Oppel); Oxford Clay: Weymouth Member
4   *Trochocyathus magnevillianus* Michelin; Oxford Clay: Stewartby Member
5   *Bositra buchii* (Roemer); Kellaways and Oxford Clay formations
6   *Hibolithes hastatus* Montfort; Oxford Clay: Stewartby and Weymouth members
7a–b *Sigaloceras calloviense* (J Sowerby); Kellaways Formation: Kellaways Sand
8a–b *Cardioceras scarburgense* (Young & Bird); Oxford Clay: Weymouth Member
9   *Genicularia vertebralis* (J de C Sowerby); Oxford Clay: Peterborough and
    Stewartby members

Plate 6 Purton Brickpit, near Swindon, Wiltshire, in 1967. The Weymouth Member of the Oxford Clay was extracted here for the manufacture of facing, engineering and common bricks until the late 1970s. Currently (1994) the clays are again being worked for the lining of landfill sites and canal repair (A11042).

shell bed rich in nuculacean bivalves and ammonites, but the term is also used in a wider sense to include the underlying metre or so of calcareous and nuculacean-rich mudstone. The distinctive serpulid *Genicularia vertebralis* (J de C Sowerby) (Plate 5:9) is a useful marker for the Peterborough Member and basal part of the overlying Stewartby Member.

The **Stewartby Member** (formerly the Middle Oxford Clay) comprises predominantly pale to medium grey, smooth or silty, calcareous mudstone. It is generally rather poorly fossiliferous, but includes beds packed with the bivalve *Bositra buchii* (Roemer) (Plate 5:5). Calcareous siltstones, up to 0.3 m thick, occur in the upper part, and are commonly associated with the oyster *Gryphaea lituola* (Lamarck). These and belemnites (particularly *Hibolithes*, Plate 5:6) are the most common fossils to be found at outcrop, because of their more robust nature and calcitic composition. Ammonites and other macrofauna, that are commonly preserved as pyritic, internal moulds, are quickly destroyed by weathering. The most distinctive bed within the member is the Lamberti Limestone which marks its top. Named after the ammonite *Quenstedtoceras lamberti* (J Sowerby), the bed was well exposed at the former Woodham brickpit, between Aylesbury and Bicester. It is a soft, pale grey or cream-coloured, silty limestone or silty, calcareous mudstone, generally about 0.3 m thick, but known to range between 0.1 and 0.7 m. It is characteristically richly fossiliferous, with a diverse ammonite fauna (including *Quenstedtoceras* with *Kosmoceras, Peltoceras, Choffatia, Euaspidoceras, Hecticoceras, Distichoceras, Alligaticeras, Reineckeia* and *Pachyceras*) preserved as broken or distorted specimens coated with dull, dark brown, powdery pyrite. Abundant bivalves, notably *Oxytoma inequivalve* (J Sowerby) and pectinids, are characteristic, and belemnites, serpulids, echinoids and gastropods are also recorded. Brickpits at Woburn Sands and Stewartby, and a temporary section at Millbrook (Figure 14), indicate that the bed is well developed in the northern part of the region. To the south-west, it has been recorded beneath gravels in pits at Stanton Harcourt, west of Oxford. Farther south-west, in Wiltshire, it is represented by a *Gryphaea/Oxytoma* shell bed with associated cementstone nodules; this has been recorded in a gravel pit at Ashton Keynes. Another useful marker bed, the Trochocyathus Band, in the middle part of the member, is characterised by an abundance of the small, solitary, cup-coral, *Trochocyathus magnevillianus* (Michelin) (Plate 5:4).

The **Weymouth Member** (formerly the Upper Oxford Clay) comprises predominantly pale grey, smooth, blocky, calcareous mudstones with thin, dark grey, carbonaceous beds showing striking interburrowing. The mudstone is typically poorly fossiliferous, but thin, calcareous siltstones, which commonly contain the large oyster *Gryphaea dilatata* (J Sowerby), occur, particularly in the upper part. The ammonite fauna (mainly cardioceratids, but also oppeliids, *Peltoceras, Euaspidoceras* and perisphinctids) is commonly pyritised, typically with small solid pyritic nuclei. As with the Stewartby Member, the most likely fossils to be found at outcrop are *Gryphaea* and belemnites.

Within the region, the **West Walton Formation** is most complete in the north-east, where up to 15 m of alternating calcareous mudstones and silty mudstones, with cementstone and siltstone nodules, are present. This succession is comparable with the type sequence of the Fens near Wisbech. South-westwards from Oxford, the upper part of the formation is replaced by the Corallian Group (Table 5; Figure 16); where the West Walton Formation

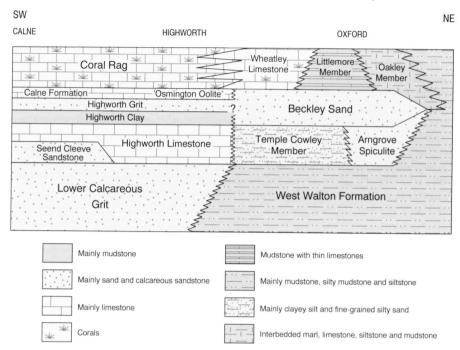

Figure 16 Stratal subdivisions of the Corallian Group. Simplified; not to scale; non-sequences not shown. In the Calne–Highworth area, there are many non-sequences, and locally one or more units may be absent.

occurs below the Corallian Group, only the most recent mapping separates the formation from the underlying Oxford Clay. In the Oxford area, the West Walton Formation contains a greater proportion of dark grey, silty, plant-rich mudstone and although the succession is incomplete, it is disproportionately thick (about 20 m). Farther south, these beds become more sandy and pass into the Lower Calcareous Grit of the Corallian Group (Figure 16). Down-dip from the outcrop, a borehole at Harwell proved the West Walton Formation to be 39 m thick. A similar thickness is probably present in the boreholes at Kingsclere and Warlingham where, however, the formation has not been differentiated from the underlying Oxford Clay, but where the combined thickness of the two formations is comparable to that at Harwell.

Large specimens of *Gryphaea dilatata* (J Sowerby) are common in the West Walton Formation; these are typically bored and encrusted by serpulids and foraminifera. Other oysters (*Lopha* and *Nanogyra*) also occur; near Ampthill, in Bedfordshire (Figure 14), beds with abundant *Nanogyra* occur in the basal part of the formation, which is much condensed and incomplete. These beds correlate with the Oakley Member of the Corallian Group of the Oxford area (Figure 16). The ammonite fauna of the West Walton Formation contains both cardioceratids and perisphinctids, although the former, particularly *Cardioceras (Plasmatoceras)*, predominate.

The **Ampthill Clay Formation** (Table 5) takes its name from Ampthill, Bedfordshire, where it was exposed during construction of the Bedford–Luton railway in the 1860s. Although the formation was formerly exposed elsewhere in the region, for example in brickpits at Brill, Buckinghamshire, and in the overburden of limestone quarries near Oxford, it is not generally well known. In much of the region, its presence has only recently been recognised; in the past, the beds were included either with the overlying Kimmeridge Clay or with the underlying Corallian Group.

Cored boreholes show that, because of Cretaceous overstep, only the lower part of the formation is present at Ampthill. However, the formation is complete to the south-west in Buckinghamshire, where it is about 20 m thick. At Wheatley, just east of Oxford, much of the formation is missing where it thins on to the limestones of the Corallian Group, and only the youngest beds (about 4 m thick) are represented (Table 5). Farther south-west, a borehole at Swindon has shown that the formation there is thicker (21 m), with fewer beds missing at the base. The formation consists of medium to dark grey mudstone and silty mudstone, and pale grey, calcareous mudstone; cementstone nodules may occur at some horizons. In the Oxford area, the uppermost beds comprise pale grey, oyster-rich mudstones with cementstones; the oysters include *Deltoideum*, *Lopha* and *Nanogyra*. To the south-west, the mudstone may be more silty and/or ferruginous and, locally, includes the Marston Ironstone (about 0.3 m thick) and Red Down Ironsand (1 m thick). The fauna is dominated by bivalves and ammonites, but at outcrop, the only fossils normally found are oysters, with *Gryphaea dilatata* (J Sowerby) characterising the lower part, and *Deltoideum delta* (Wm Smith) (Plate 7:6) the upper part. Belemnites (notably *Pachyteuthis*, Plate 8:1) may also be found together with large perisphinctid ammonites preserved in cementstone. The ammonite fauna of the mudstones is dominated by cardioceratids (*Cardioceras* in the lower part, *Amoeboceras* in the upper) on which the zonation is based (Table 5).

The **Kimmeridge Clay Formation** crops out in a relatively narrow tract from near Calne, in the south-west, to near Leighton Buzzard (Figure 14). In most areas, it is unconformably overlain by Cretaceous strata. Beyond Leighton Buzzard, it is cut out by the unconformity, though it reappears just north of the region in Cambridgeshire. In the north-east of the outcrop, the formation is generally between 40 m and 50 m thick where complete, but a borehole at Brill proved 55 m. The thickness increases south-westwards, and a borehole at Swindon proved 102 m. This thickening continues towards the south and the Wessex Basin. In the Vale of Pewsey, just south-west of the region, a borehole proved at least 230 m, and boreholes have proved 281 m at Kingsclere (possibly including a small thickness of Ampthill Clay) and more than 200 m at Warlingham (Figure 14), where the basal boundary is faulted.

Plate 7   Fossils from the Corallian Group and the Ampthill and Kimmeridge Clay formations (all natural size).

1   *Hemicidaris intermedia* (Fleming); Corallian Group
2   radiole of *Plegiocidaris florigemma* (Phillips); Corallian Group
3a–b   *Isastraea explanata* (Goldfuss); Corallian Group
4a–c   *Torquirhynchia inconstans* (J Sowerby); Ampthill or Lower Kimmeridge Clay: Inconstans Bed
5   *Cardioceras sowerbyi* Arkell; Corallian Group: Arngrove Spiculite Member
6   *Deltoideum delta* (Wm Smith); Ampthill and Lower Kimmeridge clays

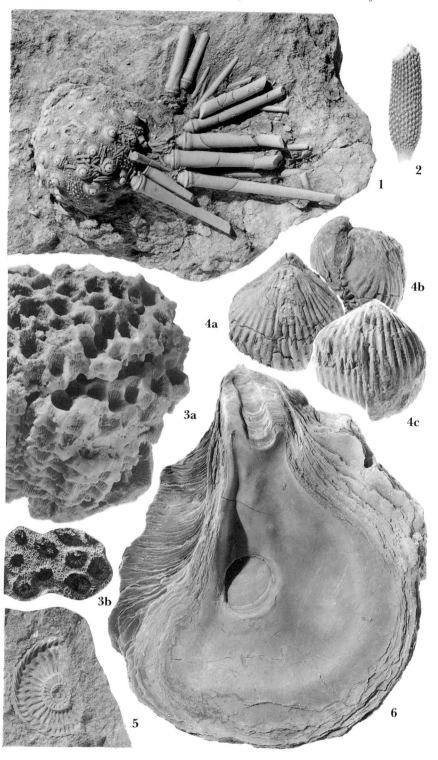

Plate 8   Fossils from the Ampthill Clay, Kimmeridge Clay and Portland formations (all natural size).

1   *Pachyteuthis abbreviata* (Miller); Ampthill Clay
2   Pliosaur vertebra; Kimmeridge Clay
3a–b   ammonite aptychal plates (*Laevaptychus*); Lower Kimmeridge Clay
4   *Aptyxiella portlandica* (J de C Sowerby); Portland Formation: Portland Stone
5a–b   *Protocardia dissimilis* (J de C Sowerby); Portland Formation: Portland Stone
6   *Pavlovia pallasioides* (Neaverson); Upper Kimmeridge Clay
7   *Nanogyra virgula* (Defrance); Kimmeridge Clay

The Kimmeridge Clay comprises rhythmic sequences of pale, calcareous mudstone, dark, shelly, kerogen-rich 'bituminous' mudstone including oil shales, and silty mudstone. The succession also includes widespread cement-stone nodule-beds. The clays were formerly worked for brickmaking at Wootton Bassett, Swindon, and at many sites near Oxford and Aylesbury. Sandstone, sand and siltstone units occur widely in the upper part of the formation. They typify deposition over the London Platform, for they are absent from thicker, basinal successions, for example at the type locality on the Dorset coast. These arenaceous units have been given various local names (Figure 17) and, in the past, have been worked for building sand at Swindon and Oxford.

The formation is richly fossiliferous, and contains abundant bivalves and also ammonites, on which the standard zonation is based (Table 5). In the Aylesbury area, the formation has been divided into several members (Figure 17) based on lithological characters, but the more widely applicable and long-standing subdivision into Lower and Upper Kimmeridge Clay is based on ammonites; these units correspond with the Lower and Upper Kimmeridgian substages of British chronostratigraphy (Table 5). The ammonite fauna

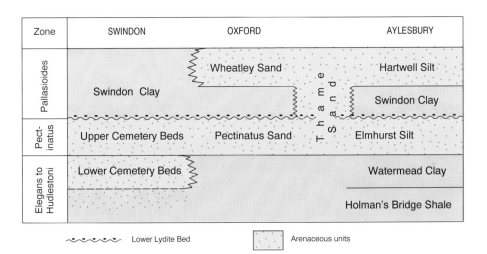

Figure 17   Stratal subdivisions (members) in the Upper Kimmeridge Clay (Upper Kimmeridgian). Not to scale.

of the Lower Kimmeridge Clay is diverse; *Pictonia, Rasenia* and *Aulacostephanus* are used as zonal indicators, but *Amoeboceras* (particularly *A. (Nannocardioceras)*), *Aspidoceras* and *Sutneria* are also readily recognised and stratigraphically useful taxa. In the Upper Kimmeridge Clay, the ammonite fauna is generally restricted to *Pectinatites* and *Pavlovia*. The type specimens of *Pectinatites wheatleyensis* Neaverson, *Pectinatites pectinatus* (Phillips) and *Pavlovia pallasioides* (Neaverson) (Plate 8:6), which give their names respectively to the Wheatleyensis, Pectinatus and Pallasioides zones of the Kimmeridgian Stage, come from this region, and the Hartwell Silt of Hartwell, near Aylesbury, is the stratotype for the last-named zone.

At outcrop, ammonites are generally rare due to weathering, although certain other fossils of stratigraphical value can be found. The large, asymmetrical brachiopod *Torquirhynchia inconstans* (J Sowerby) (Plate 7:4) is characteristic of the basal Kimmeridgian 'Inconstans Bed'. In the Oxford area, this occurs within the pale beds at the top of the Ampthill Clay; there, the base of the Kimmeridge Clay is taken at a phosphatic nodule bed at the base of the Cymodoce Zone (Table 5). The distinctive striate oyster *Nanogyra virgula* (Defrance) (Plate 8:7) is abundant in some beds in the Lower Kimmeridge Clay, and in the basal part of the Upper Kimmeridge Clay. *Laevaptychus* (the calcitic jaws or operculae of the ammonite *Aspidoceras*) and bones of marine reptiles may also be found at outcrop (Plate 8); the latter appear to have been relatively common in the shallow seas adjacent to the London Platform. Also found at outcrop are black, phosphatised bivalves (*Hiatella* and *Pleuromya*) coming from the Lower Lydite Bed, which marks the base of the Pallasioides Zone and Swindon Clay Member (Figure 17). In unweathered sections, useful markers in the Mutabilis Zone are provided by local abundances of the bivalve *Nicaniella* (Supracorallina Bed) and of pentacrinoid columnals.

CORALLIAN GROUP

The Corallian Group comprises a diverse succession of limestones, marls and sandstones. It crops out continuously from near Calne, in Wiltshire, to east of Oxford (Figure 14), producing a range of hills which contrasts with the subdued relief of the surrounding clay outcrop of the Ancholme Group (Figure 3). The group has been extensively quarried for building sand and stone (Plate 9); the local stone can be seen in the fabric of many buildings in villages along the outcrop. Many of the ancient buildings in Oxford are built from Corallian limestones quarried at nearby Wheatley and Headington; the former locality was also a major source of building stone for Windsor Castle. Most of the quarry sections are now obscured although many have been recorded in the literature and some, such as Lyehill Quarry near Wheatley and Shellingford Cross-roads Quarry near Faringdon, can still be seen.

The diversity of facies and faunas in the Corallian Group, with the image of warm tropical seas that they engender, have proved to be popular topics for study. Thus, there is an extensive literature describing the relationship of the fauna to the substrate, depositional environments and analyses of the succession in terms of depositional cycles and rhythmic sedimentation. The strata were the inspiration for many papers by W J Arkell (1904–1958), who became a world authority on Jurassic stratigraphy.

Plate 9   Quarry in the Corallian Group, Hatford, near Faringdon, Oxfordshire. Rubbly, coralliferous 'Coral Rag' limestone, overlying soft, calcareous sand of the Highworth Grit (A11918).

The base of the group is somewhat diachronous, due to north-eastward interdigitation with, and replacement by, the West Walton Formation (Table 5). Thus the oldest unit of the group, the Lower Calcareous Grit, is present only in the south-western part of the outcrop (Figure 16).

Near Oxford, boreholes at Cumnor and Garsington have proved a total thickness for the group of about 34 m and the same thickness was recorded at depth to the south, in a borehole at Harwell. Elsewhere, published thicknesses almost certainly include beds which would now be classified as the West Walton or Ampthill Clay formations, but quoted thicknesses of 26m near Uffington, 53 m at Kingsclere and 46 m at Warlingham are probably realistic. The group has also been proved in a borehole at Frindsbury, near Chatham, in the east of the region. In Wiltshire, thicknesses are variable, but are estimated to range up to 35 m; the thickest development is in the Calne area.

Rapid lateral thickness and facies changes characterise the Corallian succession, and a variety of local names have been applied to different units in the past. Some of these have been formalised as members and formations (Figure 16), but many uncertainties of correlation remain. Much of the group is richly fossiliferous. Corals (for example, *Isastraea explanata* (Goldfuss) (Plate 7.3), *Thamnasteria concinna* (Goldfuss) and *Thecosmilia annularis* (Fleming)) are generally restricted to the higher parts of the succession, in the Coral Rag.

Generally, they seem to have grown as small, isolated colonies and did not form major reefs. Gastropods, bivalves and echinoids (for example, *Plegiocidaris florigemma* (Phillips) (Plate 7:1)) are fairly widespread throughout the Corallian Group, and ammonites, particularly *Cardioceras* and *Perisphinctes*, are relatively common in some beds. The Lower Calcareous Grit yielded type specimens of *Cardioceras cordatum* (J Sowerby) which gives its name to the Cordatum Zone of the Oxfordian Stage. The Seend–Calne area of Wiltshire is the type locality for the youngest subzone of the Cordatum Zone. Locally, for example near Arngrove, in Buckinghamshire, siliceous spicules of the sponge *Rhaxella perforata* Hinde form distinctive, bluish grey, spiculitic sandstones.

PORTLAND AND PURBECK FORMATIONS

At the end of Kimmeridgian times, there was a widespread fall in sea level. In the deeper parts of the Wessex Basin, which cross the southern part of the region, Kimmeridge Clay deposition was gradually replaced by shallower-water sedimentation, culminating in marginal marine and nonmarine deposition in the late Portlandian. Farther north, over the London Platform, the upper beds of the Kimmeridge Clay were removed by erosion at this time. As a result, the **Portland Formation** unconformably overlies the Kimmeridge Clay at outcrop in the region (Table 5). The Portland Formation crops out in two main areas: at Swindon, and east of Oxford, as far north-eastwards as Stewkley, near Leighton Buzzard (Figure 14). These outcrops are the most northerly and the most extensive outcrops of the formation in Britain. In the intervening area, apart from a small outcrop at Bourton, 8 km east of Swindon, the formation is cut out by the erosional base of the Cretaceous strata; this erosion has also limited the extent of the formation at depth to the east. The maximum thickness in the areas of outcrop is about 13 m. Much greater thicknesses (47 m at Kingsclere; 41 m at Warlingham) are proved by boreholes along the southern margin of the region (Figure 2).

The formation was formerly worked from many quarries, and although virtually all are now obscured, many sections have been recorded and the formation is consequently quite well known. A two-fold subdivision of the succession into Portland Sand and Portland Stone has been used in the region, as in the type area on the Isle of Portland in Dorset, although the lithological components are different and vary locally (Figure 18).

The base of the formation is marked almost everywhere by the Upper Lydite Bed, which is characterised by abundant, rounded pebbles of black or brownish grey chert (lydites), white or yellowish quartz and quartzite, possibly derived from Palaeozoic rocks which were exposed on the London Platform. The bed also contains rarer black phosphate, including fish teeth and casts of bivalves and ammonites, derived from the topmost part of the underlying Kimmeridge Clay. The overlying Glauconitic Beds are rich in black or olive-green grains of the mineral glauconite. In the north-east, they are dominated by calcareous sandstone and siltstone, but towards the south-west, they comprise micritic limestone. An overlying, somewhat sandy limestone unit is known as the Aylesbury Limestone (or 'Rubbly Limestone') in the north-east, and as the 'Cockly Bed' at Swindon. As the latter name implies, large bivalves, in particular *Protocardia dissimilis* (J de C Sowerby) (Plate 8:5), as well as *Camptonectes*, *Fal-*

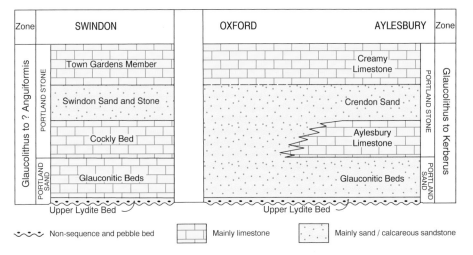

Figure 18 Stratal subdivisions of the Portland Formation in the Swindon, and Oxford–Aylesbury areas. Not to scale.

cimytilus, Pleuromya and trigoniids, are common. These limestones are overlain by an arenaceous unit, known in Oxfordshire and Buckinghamshire as the Crendon Sand, and in Wiltshire, as the 'Swindon Sand and Stone'. Between Thame and Oxford, the Aylesbury Limestone is replaced by friable sandstone and calcareous sandstone and, consequently, the Glauconitic Beds cannot be distinguished from the younger Crendon Sand in this area. The youngest unit of the Portland Formation comprises pale grey to white, fine-grained limestone, known in Buckinghamshire and Oxfordshire as the Creamy Limestone. It is predominantly micritic, particularly in the upper part. Large bivalves also occur in this unit, together with the gastropod *Aptyxiella portlandica* (J de C Sowerby), known as the 'Portland Screw' (Plate 8:4). At Swindon, the equivalent limestone and marl unit has been termed the Town Gardens Member; it was originally included with the overlying Purbeck Formation.

The Portland Formation is renowned for its giant ammonites, commonly up to 0.5 m in diameter, which may be seen as curios in gardens or as features built into walls. However, their great size and weight, and the generally poor preservation of inner whorls, make their recovery and identification difficult. Although used as the basis of the standard zonation of the Portlandian Stage (Table 5), in practice they provide more limited stratigraphical control than those in the underlying clay formations; species of *Glaucolithites, Galbanites, Crendonites* and *Titanites* characterise successive assemblages.

The **Purbeck Formation** caps the Portland Formation in only a few small areas. East of Oxford, these occur mainly between Haddenham and Stone, but there are other small isolated outcrops, for example at Brill, Long Crendon, Waddesdon and Whitchurch; the most northerly occurrence is at Stewkley, near Leighton Buzzard (Figure 14). In the south of the region, there is an isolated outcrop at Swindon. The formation was probably originally deposited over much greater areas, but removed by erosion in the Early Cretaceous. However, as with the Portland Formation, substantial thicknesses

(166 m at Kingsclere; 80 m at Warlingham) have been proved in boreholes along the southern margin of the region (Figure 2). The maximum thickness at outcrop is about 10 m.

The formation comprises limestones, interbedded with marls, clays and sandy clays. The limestones are most typically white carbonate mudstones, and may show algal laminae or stromatolitic structures, indicating very shallow or intertidal conditions. Mudcracks and possible salt pseudomorphs also occur, perhaps indicating periods of subaerial emergence. Bedding surfaces are commonly bored, indicating penecontemporaneous cementation. At Swindon, pebble beds occur throughout the succession. The fauna includes small bivalves and gastropods (for example *Valvata* and *Viviparus*), and fish and insect remains; ostracods are abundant at some horizons and, in the absence of ammonites, are used in biozonation. The fauna and lithofacies indicate a wide range of salinities, from fresh to hypersaline, and it seems likely that the formation was deposited in a very shallow, coastal or lagoonal environment.

The formation takes its name from the Isle of Purbeck in Dorset where the strata are believed to straddle the Jurassic–Cretaceous System boundary; the exact position of this boundary remains the subject of international debate. In the London and Thames Valley region, the Purbeck Formation at outcrop is believed to be exclusively Jurassic in age. In fact, the conformable and gradational nature of the contact with the underlying Portland Formation (Kerberus Zone; Table 5) may indicate that the Purbeck Formation here may be older than that in Dorset, with a relatively early onset of less-than-fully marine sedimentation. However, the thicker succession in the south of the region, on the northern edge of the Wessex Basin, is more comparable with that of Dorset and Sussex with, for example, beds of anhydrite in the basal part. An oyster-bed with *Praeexogyra distorta* (J de C Sowerby), known as the Cinder Bed (Member), and long-time candidate for the Jurassic–Cretaceous boundary bed in the Weald and Dorset, has been identified in both the Kingsclere and Warlingham boreholes.

The formation was formerly exposed in a number of quarries within the region, principally those dug to work the underlying limestones of the Portland Formation. Virtually all of these are now obscured, but the Bugle Pit at Hartwell, near Aylesbury, and the Town Gardens Quarry, Swindon, are Sites of Special Scientific Interest where the beds may still be examined.

6   Lower Cretaceous

The latest part of the Jurassic Period and the early part of the Cretaceous was a time of intense tectonic activity in Europe. These Late-Cimmerian movements were related to the northward extension of the zone of ocean-floor spreading which caused the gradual opening of the northern Atlantic. Associated uplift of north-west Europe caused the sea to retreat from the region, and the London Platform was elevated high above sea level so that the Jurassic strata suffered extensive erosion, exposing the Palaeozoic basement rocks once more.

Subsidence of the fault-bounded Wessex Basin, to the south of the region, continued, and sediments derived from the London Platform accumulated in nonmarine environments to form the Wealden Group (Table 6). Thin, correlative deposits were also laid down on the north-western flanks of the London Platform. In the early Aptian, a deepening sea covered southern England, and shallow-marine conditions were soon established over much of the region, so that the Lower Greensand, mainly of late Aptian age, was deposited over a much wider area than the Wealden sediments. A marked deepening of the sea during Albian times flooded the London Platform, and the mud which formed the Gault Formation was deposited over the whole region. Towards the end of the Albian, a different facies, the sandy Upper Greensand, was deposited in the west and south, while Gault mud continued to be deposited in the east.

WEALDEN GROUP

In latest Jurassic and earliest Cretaceous times, the sea retreated from southern England. However, marine sedimentation continued to the north-east of the London Platform and shallow-marine, pebbly sands and clays of this age are known in East Anglia, Lincolnshire and Yorkshire. The rocks of the uplifted platform, comprising both Palaeozoic basement and Jurassic cover, were subjected to subaerial erosion, and the resultant sediment was transported southward by rivers to the Wessex Basin, where it was redeposited to form the Wealden Group, locally up to 800 m thick.

Within the Wealden Group, several major sedimentary cycles can be recognised. These are probably related to the combined effects of regional sea level changes and uplift, with sand-dominated sediments prograding into the basin during times of lowered sea level, and mud-dominated sediments accumulating when sea level was higher. The group is divided into two major units, the Hastings Beds, overlain by the Weald Clay Formation. The **Hastings Beds** are dominated by siltstone and sandstone, deposited mainly by large

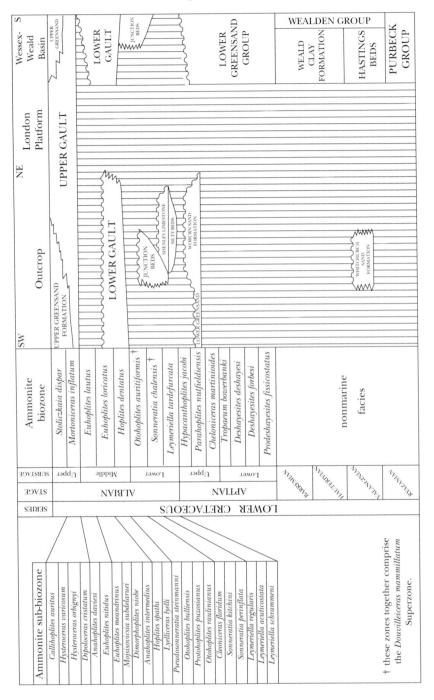

Table 6   Main strat subdivisions of the Lower Cretaceous rocks of the region

braided rivers. Some units within the Hastings Beds, and the thick **Weald Clay Formation**, are composed of mudstone. These were formed in a complex environment of swamps crossed by meandering river channels, and in lakes and lagoons of varying salinity. Emergent areas were colonised by a rich vegetation, including conifers, horsetails and ferns. Dinosaurs such as *Iguanodon*, crocodiles and some primitive mammals inhabited these areas; dinosaur footprints, isolated bones and, rarely, almost complete skeletons have been found. Molluscs and ostracods thrived in the lagoons, the faunas varying in response to changes in salinity.

As in the underlying Purbeck beds, ostracods have been used for correlation within the Wealden Group, but cannot be directly related to the international ammonite-based chronostratigraphy, as ammonites are absent from the nonmarine Wealden facies. However, plant spores and pollen, found in both the nonmarine Wealden Group and in the ammonite-bearing, marine beds of the North Sea Basin, have enabled correlation between the two regimes, proving that the Wealden Group ranges from latest Ryazanian to latest Barremian or earliest Aptian in age (Table 6).

Along the southern boundary of the region, deep boreholes at Tatsfield, Warlingham, Addington, Shalford and Kingsclere (Figure 19) show the presence of moderately thick Wealden successions (Figure 2), although these are considerably thinner than in the central part of the Wessex Basin. In Warlingham Borehole (Figure 20), the Wealden Group totals 257 m in thickness, although several faults noted in the cores may indicate that part of the succession has been cut out. The Hastings Beds, 81 m thick, are subdivided into several formations. The Ashdown Formation, at the base, is 18 m thick, and comprises mainly greenish and brownish grey silty mudstone with minor sandstones. The overlying Wadhurst Clay Formation, 19 m thick, is mainly greenish grey, shaly mudstone with silt laminae, but thin shelly beds and limestones with *Neomiodon* and *Viviparus* are common. The Tunbridge Wells Sand Formation, 43 m thick, consists mainly of alternating beds of fine-grained sandstone and silty mudstone. It is divided into Lower and Upper units by the Grinstead Clay, which is 19 m thick and resembles the Wadhurst Clay. The overlying Weald Clay Formation is 176 m thick, and is mainly pale greenish grey, laminated, silty mudstone with a number of sandstone beds, and thin beds of limestone with *Viviparus*. At the top of the Weald Clay, faunal evidence indicates a return to marine conditions, before the deposition of the Lower Greensand in Aptian times.

Northwards, the Wealden Group is overstepped by younger Cretaceous strata, and it is generally absent on the London Platform (Figure 2). However, small remnants preserved in the north-west comprise the **Whitchurch Sand Formation** (Table 6). This occurs as outliers capping hills between Oxford and Aylesbury (Figure 19) where it rests unconformably on the Portland or Purbeck formations; a probable equivalent is also known at Swindon. The thickest succession, about 20 m thick, occurs at Shotover Hill, in the eastern suburbs of Oxford, from which the original name of 'Shotover Ironsands' derives. South-eastwards, the formation is rapidly cut out by the Lower Greensand and Gault.

The Whitchurch Sand is dominated by fine- to medium-grained quartz-rich sand, which is highly ferruginous in places. It varies in colour from white, through yellow, to orange and brown, depending on the proportion of iron minerals present. The sands are generally unconsolidated, but seams and

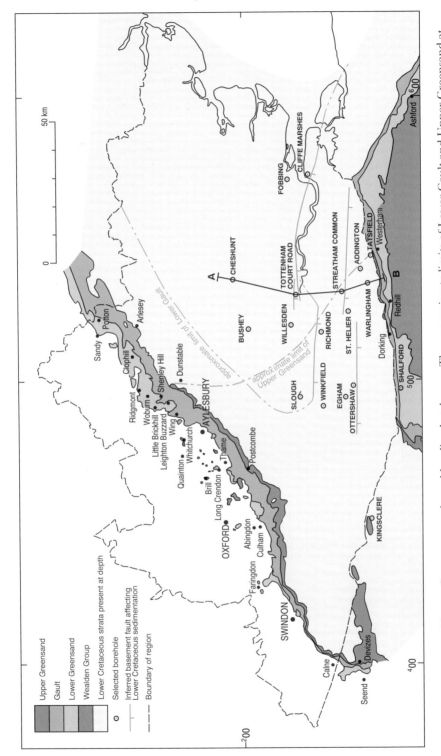

Figure 19 Outcrop of Lower Cretaceous rocks and locality sketch map. The approximate limits of Lower Gault and Upper Greensand at depth are shown; Upper Gault is present at depth throughout the region, in the area shaded. For cross-section A–B, see Figure 20.

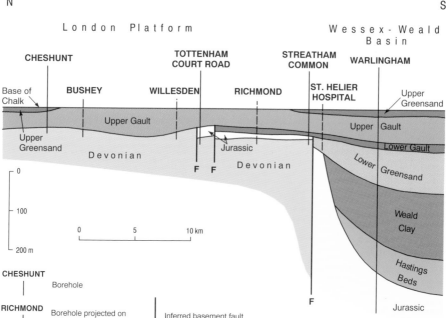

Figure 20 Diagrammatic cross-section showing thickness changes in the Lower Cretaceous succession across the southern margin of the London Platform using the base of the Chalk as an arbitrary horizontal datum. For location of boreholes and line of section, see Figure 19.

irregular masses of sandy ironstone, cemented by purplish black, brown-weathering limonite, are common. Cross-bedding, channels and other sedimentary structures within the formation are interpreted as being fluvial in origin. Lenses and beds of silt and clay are common, particularly in the lower part. These may show seatearth textures, indicating soil development and the growth of plants. Fossil rootlets and wood are fairly common. In the 1830s, a fossil tree, 12 m long, was found at Brill. Other than these plant remains, the beds are generally poorly fossiliferous, but moulds of nonmarine fossils, such as the bivalves '*Unio*' and *Neomiodon*, and gastropods including *Viviparus* (Plate 10) have been found, together with rare ostracods, the last suggesting an equivalence with the middle part of the Hastings Beds of the Weald (Valanginian). At Whitchurch and Quainton Hill, in Buckinghamshire, the formation yields marine fossils, including *Myrene* and *Laevitrigonia*, which probably indicate a temporary incursion of the sea from the north-east.

LOWER GREENSAND GROUP

Rising sea level in Aptian times flooded the Wessex Basin, and eventually a marine connection was established with the North Sea Basin around the western and northern margins of the London Platform. The central part of the platform remained as land, providing detritus which was transported by rivers into the surrounding shallow seas to form the Lower Greensand (Table 6). Generally, the thickest deposits accumulated in the Wessex Basin, which continued to subside relative to the London Platform (Figures 2 and 20). The marginal deposits of the basin have been proved by boreholes in the southern part of the region. The Lower Greensand deposited in the seaway to the north-west is represented by outcrops between Calne and Sandy (Figure 19). The outcrop is discontinuous, with the Lower Greensand absent in many places due to later, pre-Gault erosion; the preserved remnants commonly lie in erosional channels cut into the underlying Jurassic strata. These probably represent the valleys of the drowned Wealden land surface, somewhat modified by marine erosion. Locally, quite thick successions are preserved in 'troughs' which appear to have some tectonic control, probably due to reactivation of earlier faults.

Just to the south of the region, near Devizes (Figure 19), the Lower Greensand comprises highly ferruginous sands and gravels, known as the **Seend Ironsand**. At Seend, the beds were formerly worked as an iron ore. In the last century, an extensive fossil fauna was collected from the workings; this included brachiopods, bivalves, gastropods, echinoids and ammonites indicating the Upper Aptian *Parahoplites nutfieldiensis* Zone (Plate 10). It is likely that most of the Lower Greensand in the western part of the region is of this age. However, just east of Calne, the Lower Greensand is of markedly different facies, comprising clean, white, cross-bedded fine- to medium-grained quartz sands, up to 12 m thick. These are the **Calne Sands** which may be somewhat younger than the Seend Ironsand. They are restricted to a relatively small area, and are overstepped by the Gault both to the north and south.

North-eastwards towards Swindon, the Lower Greensand is generally absent, although locally small patches are preserved between the Gault and the Kimmeridge Clay. On the M4 motorway south of Swindon, for example, these strata comprise less than 2 m of highly ferruginous sand containing cobbles of Portland limestone.

At Faringdon, about 15 km north-east of Swindon, the Lower Greensand thickens dramatically, infilling a south-east-trending erosional trough, that

Plate 10   Fossils from the Whitchurch Sand, Lower Greensand and Junction Beds (all natural size except 9a–b ($\times$ 0.5)).

1   *Ampullospira* cf. *incisa* (Blake); Whitchurch Sand Formation
2   '*Unio*' sp. ; Whitchurch Sand Formation
3   *Neomiodon sublaevis* (Roemer); Whitchurch Sand Formation
4   *Gemmarcula menardi* (Lamarck); Lower Greensand: Faringdon Sponge Gravels
5   *Oxytoma cornuelianum* (d'Orbigny); Lower Greensand: Faringdon Sponge Gravels
6a–b   *Rhaphidonema faringdonense* (Sharpe); Lower Greensand: Faringdon Sponge Gravels
7   *Cyclothyris latissima* (J de C Sowerby); Lower Greensand: Faringdon Sponge Gravels
8   *Toucasia lonsdalii* (J de C Sowerby); Lower Greensand
9a–b   *Parahoplites nutfieldiensis* (J Sowerby); Lower Greensand
10   *Hyposalenia wrighti* Desor; Lower Greensand: Faringdon Sponge Gravels
11a–b   *Rectithyris shenleyensis* (Lamplugh & Walker); Lower Greensand: Shenley Limestone
12   *Douvilleiceras leightonense* Casey; Junction Beds

(× 0.5)

cuts down through the Kimmeridge and Ampthill clays, into the underlying Corallian Group. The lower part of the sequence comprises the **Faringdon Sponge Gravels**, some 50 m in thickness, which consist of cross-bedded pebbly sands and highly fossiliferous gravels, with a basal pebble bed containing derived Jurassic fossils. The gravels contain abundant fossils, notably calcareous sponges, as well as polyzoans, brachiopods and echinoids (Plate 10). Above the Sponge Gravels, some 30 m of sand and clay with chert and ironstone occur; these beds have yielded ammonites of the *nutfieldiensis* Zone. At Baulking, a few kilometres south-east of Faringdon, these upper beds include two seams of fuller's earth clay. Fuller's earth is formed from the decomposition of volcanic ash in a marine environment, and its presence at Baulking indicates that volcanoes were active at no great distance from southern England. Vents of equivalent age are known in the Netherlands and North Atlantic.

The Lower Greensand is overstepped by the Gault immediately east of Baulking, but it reappears near Culham (Figure 19). Patchy remnants occur in the Oxford–Aylesbury area where they consist predominantly of poorly sorted, red, pebbly, coarse-grained sand. Generally, these beds are only a few metres thick, with a maximum of some 16 m at Milton Common, near Thame. Fossils are rare, but at Thame and Quainton Hill, brown, ferruginous, coarse-grained 'gritty' sandstones contain a fauna closely similar to that from Seend. The fossils include rudist bivalves, such as *Toucasia lonsdalii* (J de C Sowerby) (Plate 10), which provide evidence of a temporary link with more southern seas in *nutfieldiensis* Zone times.

The Lower Greensand is absent for some distance north-eastwards from Aylesbury, but is present at Leighton Buzzard (Figure 19), and from there extends beyond the boundary of the region. The deposits in this area comprise the **Woburn Sand Formation**, which infills a large basin, cut into Late Jurassic mudstones. The Woburn Sand is generally 30 to 60 m in thickness, but is up to 120 m thick north of Leighton Buzzard.

Where fully developed, the Woburn Sand Formation can be subdivided into several units (Figure 21). The lower and greater part consists of fine- to medium-grained, yellowish, cross-bedded sands with some thin lenses of secondary iron-pan and, in the Woburn area, seams of impure fuller's earth (Plate 23). These beds, known as the 'Lower Woburn Sand' or 'Brown Sands', are similar to the *nutfieldiensis* Zone beds of Baulking and the northern Weald. At Clophill, the ammonite *Parahoplites nutfieldiensis* (J Sowerby) has been found (Plate 10:9). A basal pebbly bed, which rests upon the eroded Jurassic surface, was formerly exposed at Little Brickhill, Ridgmont and Potton. It is highly fossiliferous and is famous for its well-preserved brachiopod fauna. It also yields derived Upper Jurassic fossils and, at Potton, Early Aptian ammonites indicate pre-*nutfieldiensis* Zone incursions of the sea of which no other evidence remains.

The overlying 'Upper Woburn Sand' or 'Silver Sands', are up to about 20 m thick. They consist of poorly sorted, coarse-grained, strongly cross-bedded sands, with some lenses of secondary iron-pan. The sands are of considerable economic importance and have been extensively quarried around Leighton Buzzard (Plate 11). The bedding of the sands is characteristic of sand waves, which form in strongly current-swept seaways. Similar sand-wave deposits occur in the Folkestone Formation of the Weald, and the Silver Sands are

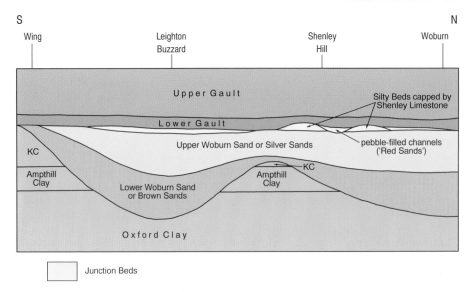

Figure 21   Schematic cross-section showing the Lower Cretaceous succession in the Leighton Buzzard area, and its relationship to the underlying Jurassic strata. Not to scale. For location see Figure 19. KC: Kimmeridge Clay.

probably of approximately the same age, belonging mainly to the Late Aptian *Hypacanthoplites jacobi* Zone (Table 6). The Calne Sands of Wiltshire have been interpreted as an isolated remnant of these deposits. The Silver Sands yield plant remains, including trunks of large coniferous trees, which bear witness to the inundation of coastal areas by the advancing Late Aptian sea.

The 'Junction Beds' rest on the eroded surface of the Silver Sands in the Leighton Buzzard area. These are a thin but variable succession, forming the topmost unit of the Woburn Sands, and are overlain by mudstone of the Gault Formation (Figure 21). At Shenley Hill, just north of Leighton Buzzard, the greater part of the Junction Beds comprises thinly bedded, muddy and carbonaceous silts, up to 3.5 m thick. These 'Silty Beds' have been interpreted as tidal flat deposits, but they may alternatively have been deposited in a shallow, quiet-water, land-marginal, marine lagoon. In the most complete sequences, thin gritty ironstone at the top of the silts locally contains lenses of cream-coloured, pebbly and micritic limestone. This 'Shenley Limestone' is commonly highly fossiliferous, with a fauna dominated by brachiopods, such as *Rectithyris shenleyensis* (Lamplugh & Walker) (Plate 10:11) and crinoids indicating a relatively shallow, clear and warm marine environment. Rare ammonites indicate the Early Albian *Leymeriella tardefurcata* Zone, *L. regularis* Subzone (Table 6). Subsequent erosion cut channels through the Silty Beds, leaving a series of east–west- trending knolls capped by blocks of resistant Shenley Limestone. Ammonites within reworked material between these blocks show that the erosion occurred during *Otohoplites auritiformis* Zone (*O. bulliensis* Subzone) times. The channels between the knolls are infilled with brown pebbly sands, known as the 'Red Sands', which contain ironstone fragments and concretions. A thin

Plate 11   Woburn Sand Formation, Leighton Buzzard, Bedfordshire. The upper part of the formation is exposed in a number of pits on the outskirts of Leighton Buzzard. Here, the 'Silver Sands' exhibit large-scale cross-bedding and other sedimentary structures, characteristic of deposition in a shallow sea. At the top of the face, the basal beds of the Gault Formation can be seen (A 14474).

layer of ironstone caps both the knolls and intervening Red Sand channel-deposits; it was formed during the latest part of the *O. auritiformis* Zone (*Pseudosonneratia steinmanni* Subzone). It is probable that the Silty Beds and Shenley Limestone were originally much more extensive in Bedfordshire and Buckinghamshire; a remnant of Shenley Limestone has been recorded at Long Crendon, near Thame, some 30 km south-west of Shenley Hill.

South of Shenley Hill, the Junction Beds are of somewhat different facies, indicating deposition in more-open water. Above the eroded surface of the Silver Sands, a pebbly, silty or ferruginous sand or gritty clay, contains several layers of gritty, phosphatic nodules. These contain reworked ammonites indicating several phases of Early Albian erosion, during the *L. regularis* Subzone and *Sonneratia chalensis* Zone. South-west of Leighton Buzzard, above these mixed layers, a further phosphatic nodule bed contains ammonites of the *steinmanni* Subzone and earliest *Hoplites dentatus* Zone, representing the final phase of pre-Gault erosion seen on Shenley Hill.

Elsewhere in the region, boreholes indicate that Lower Greensand is generally absent over the London Platform. However, in the Fobbing-Cliffe Marshes area (Figure 19), up to 29 m of Lower Greensand are preserved in a trough. South of an inferred fault, running approximately along the lower Thames valley from Cliffe, beneath central London, to near Slough, very thin

Lower Greensand occurs locally, as proved in boreholes at Cliffe, Richmond, Ottershaw and Winkfield (Figure 19). Fossils from the base of these beds indicate the *nutfieldiensis* Zone, and attest to a widespread transgression which occurred at that time.

At Streatham, close to the southern margin of the London Platform, a borehole showed that the Lower Greensand is absent. Other boreholes, to the south of the faulted margin of the Wessex Basin (for example St Helier, Addington, Tatsfield and Warlingham; Figure 19), have proved a moderately thick Lower Greensand sequence, albeit rather thinner than the 200 m or more developed elsewhere in the Weald. At Warlingham, for example, the Lower Greensand is 94 m thick (Figure 20), and all the formations of the full succession of the Wessex Basin appear to be present, although the classification is somewhat uncertain because of poor core recovery. The succession commences with 6.3 m of silty sands of the Atherfield Formation, and passes up through 28 m of greenish grey sands, sandstones and thin sandy clays assigned to the Hythe Formation. These strata, of Early Aptian age, are not fully represented elsewhere in the region (Table 6). The succeeding Sandgate Formation comprises fine-grained, glauconitic sands, 1.2 m thick. Elsewhere in the Weald, it more typically comprises glauconitic, argillaceous sands and mudstones. It rests disconformably on the Hythe Formation, and was deposited during the *nutfieldiensis* Zone transgression. The succeeding Folkestone Formation, 58.5 m thick, comprises coarse sands of *jacobi* Zone age, and includes sand-wave deposits like those in the Silver Sands of Bedfordshire.

GAULT AND UPPER GREENSAND FORMATIONS

There was a marked deepening of the sea in Mid Albian times so that mudstones of the Gault Formation rest non-sequentially on the Lower Greensand, overstepping it towards the London Platform to rest successively on Jurassic and Palaeozoic rocks (Figures 2 and 20). The Gault is thus the earliest Cretaceous formation to extend across the entire platform. It crops out in a narrow tract of country from Wiltshire to Bedfordshire, and to the east is present at depth throughout the rest of the region (Figures 1 and 19). Where fully developed, the Gault varies between about 65 and 90 m in thickness, but decreases eastwards, to about 56m in Essex and north Kent, where the oldest part of the succession is missing. The Upper Greensand replaces the youngest part of the Gault in the south and west of the region, and locally extends farther eastward.

The **Gault Formation** consists mainly of grey mudstone with variable amounts of silt, and in general, is more silty in the west of the region. A distinction is made between dark grey mudstone of the Lower Gault, which is of Mid Albian age, and paler, more calcareous mudstone of the Upper Gault, which is Late Albian in age (Table 6). Small, greyish buff concretions or nodules rich in calcium phosphate, may be developed around fossils or burrows, and seams of bluish black, commonly polished, phosphatic pebbles and reworked fossils mark non-sequences; these represent phosphatic debris winnowed from the sediment during periods of erosive current action.

The Gault contains a fauna dominated by bivalves and ammonites, which are usually preserved as crushed, aragonitic shells. These are rapidly

destroyed by weathering, so that generally only the calcitic guards of belemnites (notably *Neohibolites minimus* Miller; Plate 12:6) and phosphatised fossils
remain in the soil or in shallow exposures. In general, the Lower Gault is
characterised by hoplitid ammonites, such as *Hoplites dentatus* (J Sowerby),
Anahoplites intermedius Spath, *Dimorphoplites niobe* Spath and *Euhoplites* spp. The
Upper Gault contains a high proportion of brancoceratids and mortonicer-
atids (for example, *Hysteroceras* and *Mortoniceras*), together with hoplitids such
as *Euhoplites, Epihoplites* and *Callihoplites*. The bivalve *Birostrina concentrica*
(Parkinson) is a common and characteristic form in the Lower Gault, but is
replaced by *B. sulcata* (Parkinson) in the *Mortoniceras inflatum* Zone (*Dipoloceras cristatum* and *Hysteroceras orbignyi* subzones). *B. concentrica* recurs in the
Hysteroceras varicosum Subzone (Plate 12).

The **Lower Gault** is present at outcrop, and also at depth in the southern
part of the region, but is nowhere more than 10 to 15 m thick. It is absent on
the central part of the London Platform (Figures 19 and 20), removed by
erosion in the late Albian. The basal metre or so of the Lower Gault is
commonly glauconitic, silty and sandy, with layers of phosphatic nodules and
fossils, indicating periods of current scour in relatively shallow water. The succeeding beds are dark grey, generally fissile, pyritic mudstones with sporadic
seams of phosphatic nodules, and are highly fossiliferous. In the western part
of the region, the Lower Gault was formerly well exposed in brickpits at
Devizes just to the south of the region, at Badbury Wick near Swindon, and at
Culham and Thame in Oxfordshire. These sections showed that the Lower
Gault is about 12 m thick, and mainly represents the *Hoplites dentatus* and
early *Euhoplites loricatus* zones; younger Lower Gault is probably absent.
Farther north-east, the Lower Gault is exposed in the extensive pits dug for
the Woburn Sands at Leighton Buzzard (Plate 11). It blankets the channel
and knoll topography of the eroded Junction Beds (Figure 21); although
locally up to 10 m in thickness, it may be no more than 2 or 3 m thick over
the knolls. The basal beds locally consist of fissile, red to greenish grey
mudstone with crinoid debris. This 'Cirripede Bed', together with a glauconitic loamy sand with black, phosphatic nodules which occurs patchily in

Plate 12   Fossils from the Gault and Upper Greensand (all natural size except
1 ($\times$ 0.5) and 2 ($\times$ 0.5)).

1   *Mortoniceras (M.) albense* Spath; Upper Gault
2   *Hoplites spathi* Breistroffer; Lower Gault
3   *Hoplites* aff. *dentatus* (J Sowerby); Lower Gault
4   *Euhoplites trapezoidalis formosa* Spath; Upper Gault
5   *Hamites intermedius* J Sowerby; Upper Gault
6   *Neohibolites minimus* (Miller); Upper Gault
7   *Birostrina concentrica* (Parkinson) (late form); Upper Gault
8   *Hysteroceras orbignyi* Spath; Upper Gault
9   *Anchura (Perissoptera) parkinsoni* Mantell; Upper Greensand
10   *Epiaster* cf. *crassissimus* (Defrance); Upper Greensand
11   *Aucellina* sp. *gryphaeoides* (J de C Sowerby) group; Upper Greensand
12   *Aucellina* sp. *uerpmanni* Polutoff group; Upper Greensand
13   *Nanonavis carinatum* (J Sowerby); Upper Greensand
14   *Birostrina sulcata* (Parkinson); Upper Gault
15   *Callihoplites* aff. *vraconensis* (Pictet & Campiche); Upper Greensand

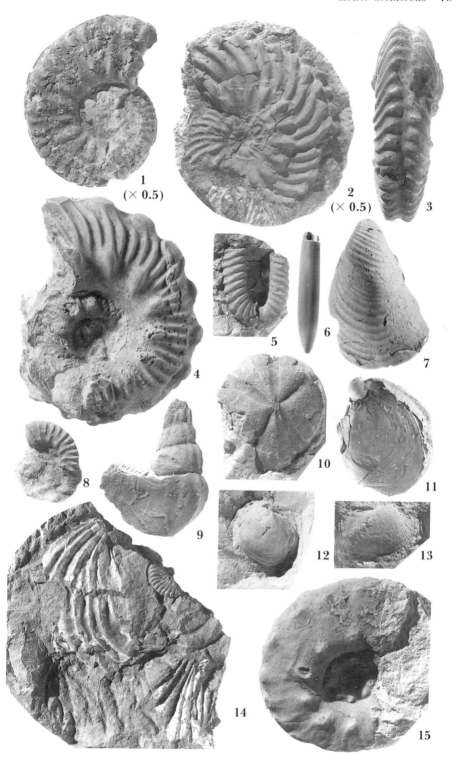

the southern part of Shenley Hill, were once thought to form part of the Junction Beds (Lower Albian), but are now known to be the oldest Gault beds, belonging to the *Hoplites dentatus* Zone (*H. spathi* Subzone). At Leighton Buzzard, younger Lower Gault of the *loricatus* Zone is present, but the succeeding *Euhoplites lautus* Zone is absent beneath the transgressive Upper Gault. A similar sequence occurs in the southern part of the region, where Lower Gault is known from boreholes south of the Thames, for example at Egham, Richmond and in the Cliffe area, and also at outcrop just south of the region. Only locally, as at Egham, is the *lautus* Zone present (Table 6).

Some tectonic activity occurred during the earliest part of the Late Albian (*Mortoniceras inflatum* Zone, *Dipoloceras cristatum* Subzone). This involved slight uplift of the London Platform, some very gentle folding, and reactivation of pre-existing faults, including those at the edge of the Wessex Basin (Figure 19). This caused current-winnowing of the upper surface of the Lower Gault throughout southern England, and its total removal from the central part of the London Platform to the north of the fault system inferred along the Thames valley. Material reworked from these beds occurs as a phosphatic pebble bed which overlies the eroded Lower Gault surface. Following this erosional event, a general rise in sea level led to deposition of Upper Gault throughout the region. North of the Thames, where the Lower Gault is absent, Upper Gault rests directly upon pre-Cretaceous rocks (Table 6; Figure 20).

The **Upper Gault** is much thicker than the Lower Gault. It reaches a maximum of perhaps 75 m in eastern Buckinghamshire, but is more generally about 50 m thick, and possibly less than 25 m in the more westerly parts of the region. Some of the thinner successions are condensed sequences, whilst others result from the passage of the uppermost beds into Upper Greensand facies, or the loss of the uppermost beds beneath the erosional base of the succeeding Cambridge Greensand or Glauconitic Marl (Chalk Group).

Around Swindon, in the west of the region, the basal Upper Gault consists of 16 m of sandy clays of the *Hysteroceras orbignyi* and *H. varicosum* subzones (*Mortoniceras inflatum* Zone). At outcrop in the north of the region, Upper Gault of the *cristatum* and *orbignyi* subzones, and basal *varicosum* Subzone, is highly condensed, being no more than 2 to 3 m thick. It contains several phosphatic pebble beds that were worked (as 'coprolites') in the nineteenth century for fertilizer manufacture. These strata are well exposed in the Leighton Buzzard area. The thickness of the overlying part of the *varicosum* Subzone there is uncertain, but further east at Arlesey (Figure 19), a borehole showed the subzone to total about 7 m in thickness and, just south of the region, the clays of the *varicosum* Subzone attain a thickness of 42 m in the Dorking–Redhill area, although underlying Upper Gault beds are thin.

During the Late Albian, erosion of uplifted land areas beyond the Wessex Basin, provided a source of coarser sediment which progressively encroached into the region to form the **Upper Greensand Formation**. This comprises interbedded sands and sandstones, commonly speckled with glauconite. Some of the sandstones contain pale grey chert concretions. Locally, towards the top of the succession, the 'Malmstone' is a peculiar type of sandstone made up largely of siliceous sponge spicules in a secondary siliceous cement. The formation is not generally very fossiliferous, but some beds contain small bivalves such as *Aucellina* (Plate 12:12), and moulds of ammonites.

The base of the Upper Greensand is markedly diachronous; the arenaceous sediments reached the western parts of the region during *varicosum* Subzone times, whilst clays continued to be deposited in the northern and eastern parts (Table 6). Submarine current erosion associated with minor uplift during the final part of the *Mortoniceras inflatum* Zone (*Callihoplites auritus* Subzone), produced a widespread glauconitic and phosphatic pebble bed. This lies within the Upper Greensand in the west of the region, but within Gault facies to the east of Swindon. Upper Greensand deposition spread rapidly eastwards during the succeeding *Stoliczkaia dispar* Zone, and by the end of the Albian extended across much of the region.

The Upper Greensand reaches its maximum thickness of some 25 m between Devizes and Postcombe (Figure 19). Farther to the north-east, the formation thins markedly, and is replaced by silty and finely micaceous mudstone of the Gault. It appears to die out altogether near Dunstable and, in the northern part of the region, calcareous muds of the Upper Gault continued to be deposited throughout the remainder of the Late Albian. A borehole at Arlesey proved about 43 m of mudstone of *auritus* Subzone and early *dispar* Zone age. The uppermost part of the sequence is exposed in a nearby brickpit where the top the Gault is an erosion surface, surmounted by Cenomanian Cambridge Greensand containing late Albian fossils derived from the Gault.

The eastward extent of the Upper Greensand facies at depth is generalised in Figure 19, but is poorly known in detail. This is partly because the Glauconitic Marl, at the base of the succeeding Chalk Group, may have been misidentified as Upper Greensand in some borehole logs. Nevertheless, it appears that the Upper Greensand is absent at Bushey and in west London but, farther east, it reappears between the Chalk and Gault at Cheshunt and at Fobbing. This patchy distribution may be a result of erosional dissection, prior to deposition of the Chalk Group. The formation is widely represented south of the River Thames. In this area, arenaceous sedimentation commenced in *dispar* Zone times, following formation of the *auritus* Subzone pebble bed (Table 6). At outcrop in the western Weald, just beyond the southern margin of the region, the Upper Greensand is entirely of *dispar* Zone age, but is replaced by Gault in the Westerham area. The *auritus* Subzone pebble bed continues eastwards in Gault facies in borings in north Kent and south Essex.

7 Upper Cretaceous: Chalk Group

In Late Cretaceous times, rising sea level progressively inundated the whole of Europe. Decreasing amounts of terrigenous material were supplied from the shrinking landmasses and increasingly pure calcareous pelagic sediments, eventually to become chalk, were deposited. Isotope studies, and the presence of organisms such as corals, brachiopods and echinoderms, indicate that the Late Cretaceous sea was of normal salinity, but significantly warmer than at present. At its maximum, the depth is believed to have been between 200 and 600 m, although it was probably somewhat shallower over the London Platform.

The Chalk Group, as the name implies, is composed predominantly of chalk, a very fine-grained, pure limestone, which may contain more than 98 per cent calcium carbonate as low magnesian calcite. The remainder comprises clays, such as montmorillonite and illite, with small amounts of very fine-grained quartz. Chalk is typically soft and uncemented, but where it is hardened at some horizons, it may be referred to as chalkstone. Up to 90 per cent of the carbonate sediment is composed of minute calcite crystals, a few microns across, derived from the disintegration of coccoliths, which are the skeletons of unicellular algae (coccolithophorids) that thrived in the Late Cretaceous seas. Within this coccolith 'flour', larger particles of calcite comprise complete coccoliths and other nannofossils, microfossils including calcispheres (the calcareous skeletons of certain dinoflagellates), foraminifera and ostracod valves. Finely comminuted shell debris, particularly prisms of inoceramid bivalves, also occurs; at some current-winnowed horizons, it may reach rock-building proportions.

Throughout much of the Chalk succession, the invertebrate macrofauna (Plate 13) is of low diversity, and those fossils preserved are mainly forms with calcite shells, such as brachiopods, echinoderms and some bivalves, notably inoceramids. Any aragonite shells, such as those of gastropods, ammonites

Plate 13   Fossils of the Chalk Group (all natural size, except 1 ($\times$ 3) and 4 ($\times$ 0.75)).

1   *Terebratulina lata* (R Etheridge); Middle Chalk
2   *Micraster coranguinum* (Leske); Upper Chalk
3   *Marsupites testudinarius* (Schlotheim); Upper Chalk
4   *Mytiloides mytiloides* (Mantell); Middle Chalk
5   *Hyphantoceras reussianum* (d'Orbigny); Upper Chalk: Chalk Rock
6   *Actinocamax plenus* (Blainville); Lower Chalk: Plenus Marls
7   *Inoceramus crippsi* Mantell; Lower Chalk
8a–c   *Schloenbachia varians* (J Sowerby); Lower Chalk
9a–b   *Orbirhynchia cuvieri* (d'Orbigny); Middle Chalk

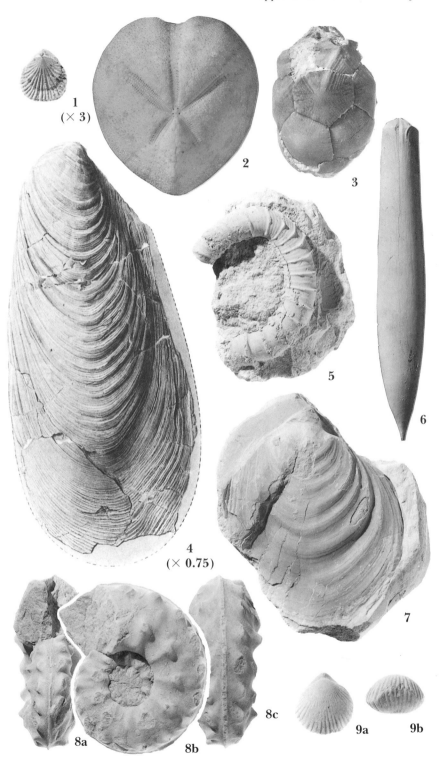

1
(× 3)

2

3

4
(× 0.75)

5

6

7

8a

8b

8c

9a

9b

and most bivalves, have generally been destroyed by solution, and such fossils are preserved only in the more argillaceous chalks forming the lower part of the Chalk Group, or in hardgrounds where they are represented by hollow moulds. Because of the extreme rarity of ammonites, the traditional zonation of the higher part of the succession is based on a combination of brachiopods, bivalves, crinoids and echinoids (Table 7). In most cases, the precise relationship of these zones to the international ammonite zones is uncertain. Recently, there has been increasing use of a zonation based on inoceramid bivalves, which are fairly common throughout the succession, and have an almost worldwide distribution. However, detailed correlation is best achieved using lithological marker bands, some of which are traceable over much of southern England.

The Chalk Group was originally deposited throughout the region, covering both the London Platform and the surrounding basinal areas. During the Alpine tectonic phases of the Cainozoic Era, the southern part of the region was folded into a broad, eastward-pitching asymmetrical syncline known as the London Basin. Within the region, the principal outcrop of the Chalk lies on the gently dipping north-western limb of this fold, where it forms the Marlborough Downs in Wiltshire, the Berkshire Downs, and the Chiltern Hills of Buckinghamshire and Hertfordshire (Figure 22). In the south of the region, the Chalk of the North Downs lies on the southern limb. There, deep faults which define the southern margin of the London Platform were reactivated, and the beds dip relatively steeply (Figure 2); dips as high as 55° have been recorded in the Hog's Back Monocline, between Farnham and Dorking.

The Chalk is present at depth throughout the intervening tract beneath London and Essex, where it is overlain by up to 200 m of post-Cretaceous beds. Locally in this area, the major synclinal structure is complicated by several intersecting minor folds, which lie both parallel, and at right angles to, the main east–west axis of the basin. These are probably related to faults in the underlying Lower Cretaceous and Palaeozoic rocks (Figures 1 and 5). For example, periclinal structures bring the Chalk to the surface in the Purfleet–Grays area on the north bank of the River Thames, and in the Cliffe Marshes on the Kent side. At Chislehurst, artificial caves have been cut in an upfolded inlier of Chalk, and a pericline at Windsor forms the prominent hill upon which the castle is built.

The Chalk succession over the London Platform is somewhat attenuated compared with that in adjoining areas of southern England, although some parts, notably the basal beds in the Chilterns, are relatively thicker. During Turonian and Coniacian times, the area from Wiltshire extending north-eastwards to the southern part of the Chiltern Hills was an area of restricted sedimentation (the 'Berkshire–Chilterns shelf'), where thin, highly condensed successions with hardgrounds (the Chalk Rock and Top Rock) are developed.

In the early Palaeogene, extensive erosion took place throughout the region. As a result, the youngest part of the Upper Chalk was removed, and the chalk is much thinner than in some other parts of England; typical maximum values of the order of 200 m contrast with over 400 m in Hampshire and Norfolk. In general, the most complete successions are preserved near the axis of the London Basin syncline.

The Chalk successions exposed in cliff sections on the coast of Sussex, between Brighton and Eastbourne, and of Kent, between Folkestone, Dover

Table 7 Main stratal subdivisions of the Chalk Group in the region.

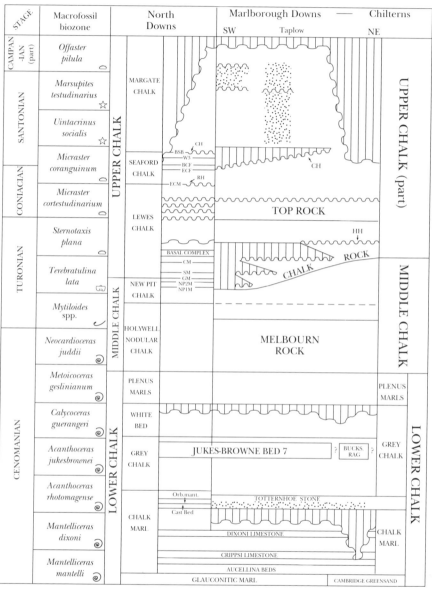

STAGE	Macrofossil biozone	North Downs	Marlborough Downs		Chilterns
			SW	Taplow	NE
CAMPANIAN (part)	*Offaster pilula* ⌒				
SANTONIAN	*Marsupites testudinarius* ☆	MARGATE CHALK			
	Uintacrinus socialis ☆				
CONIACIAN	*Micraster coranguinum* ⌒	SEAFORD CHALK			
	Micraster cortestudinarium ⌒		TOP ROCK		
TURONIAN	*Sternotaxis plana* ⌒	LEWES CHALK			
	Terebratulina lata 🝙	NEW PIT CHALK			
	Mytiloides spp. ᴗ				
	Neocardioceras juddii ◎	HOLYWELL NODULAR CHALK	MELBOURN ROCK		
CENOMANIAN	*Metoicoceras geslinianum* ◎	PLENUS MARLS			PLENUS MARLS
	Calycoceras guerangeri ◎	WHITE BED			GREY CHALK
	Acanthoceras jukesbrownei ◎	GREY CHALK	JUKES-BROWNE BED 7	BUCKS. RAG	
	Acanthoceras rhotomagense ◎	CHALK MARL	TOTTERNHOE STONE		CHALK MARL
	Mantelliceras dixoni ◎		DIXONI LIMESTONE		
	Mantelliceras mantelli ◎		CRIPPSI LIMESTONE / AUCELLINA BEDS / GLAUCONITIC MARL		CAMBRIDGE GREENSAND

◎	ammonite	BCF	Bedwell's Columnar Flint Band	RH	Rochester Hardground
ᴗ	bivalve	BSB	Barrois Sponge Bed	SM	Southerham Marl
		CH	Clandon Hardground	W3	Whitaker's 3-inch Flint
		CM	Caburn Marl		
🝙	brachiopod	ECF	East Cliff Semitabular Flint	∿∿	Hardground
		ECM	East Cliff Marl		
☆	crinoid	GM	Glynde Marl	⌐∿	Erosion surface
		HH	Hitch Wood Hardground		
⌒	echinoid	NP1M	New Pit Marl 1	▓	Phosphatic chalk
		NP2M	New Pit Marl 2		
		Orb.mant	*Orbirhynchia mantelliana* Band	▥	Strata absent

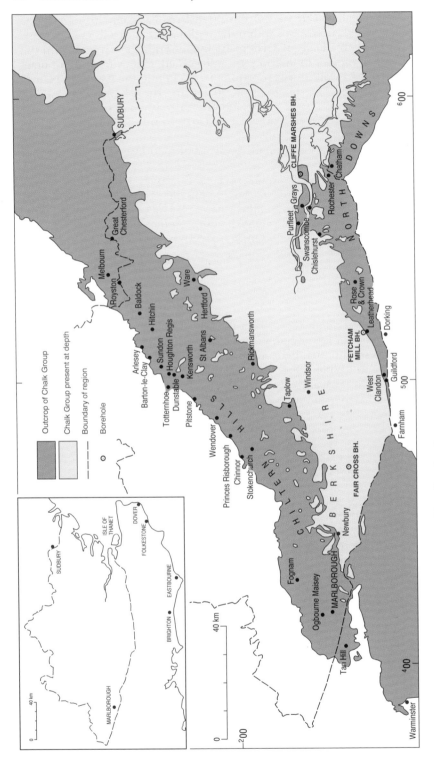

Figure 22 Outcrop of the Chalk Group and locality sketch map.

and the Isle of Thanet (Figure 22) form standards for comparison with the somewhat modified successions within the region, where details come mainly from quarries. Many details of sections no longer visible are recorded in the literature, and a number of quarries are still worked, mainly for cement manufacture, notably in south Essex, north Kent, and along the Chilterns escarpment. Little detailed information is available for the Chalk Group where concealed in the central part of the London Basin, although cored boreholes at Fetcham Mill, Leatherhead, and at Fair Cross, south of Reading, provide data for the west.

The Chalk Group has traditionally been subdivided into three formations, the Lower Chalk, Middle Chalk and Upper Chalk (Table 7). The Lower Chalk is made up of impure, argillaceous chalk, which is particularly clayey (up to 30 per cent) in the lower part. It is generally grey when fresh, due to finely disseminated pyrite, but weathers to shades of buff. In contrast, both the Middle and Upper Chalk comprise pure, white chalks, and for this reason, an alternative classification for southern England combines them into a single 'White Chalk Formation'.

LOWER CHALK

The Lower Chalk is about 65 to 75 m thick throughout most of the region, and locally somewhat less, notably in north Hertfordshire. The Lower Chalk is divisible into several members, most of which are recognisable throughout southern England (Table 7; Figure 23).

The **Glauconitic Marl**, at the base of the Lower Chalk, is present throughout the western and southern parts of the region. It comprises a sandy marl, rich in pelletal glauconite and containing phosphatic pebbles, and ranges from a few tens of centimetres to several metres in thickness. It rests on a strongly burrowed surface of Upper Greensand or (locally in the North Downs) on Upper Gault. In the Chilterns, the Glauconitic Marl thins progressively to the north-east of Princes Risborough, and becomes unrecognisable near Dunstable (Figures 22 and 23). In the north-eastern part of the region, the base of the Chalk is marked by the **Cambridge Greensand**, which terminates abruptly south-westwards, apparently against a fault or monoclinal structure, near Barton-le-Clay. It is a glauconitic, micaceous marl with abundant phosphatised pebbles, which rests unconformably on Upper Gault. The pebbles, like those in the Gault, are popularly known as 'coprolites', and were formerly worked for phosphate. Many are reworked fossils from the Gault; these include ammonites, the bivalve *Aucellina* (Plate 12:12) and large brachiopods. The Cambridge Greensand also contains non-phosphatised, indigenous fossils of Cenomanian age, including small brachiopods and *Aucellina*.

The **Chalk Marl** succession is fairly uniform throughout the region, although the lower part is relatively thicker in the Chilterns than in the North Downs, and the top of the succession is missing in the Chilterns due to a non-sequence (Table 7; Figure 23). In Fetcham Mill Borehole, the Chalk Marl is abnormally condensed. The Chalk Marl is perhaps the most fossiliferous part of the Chalk Group, and is particularly rich in sponges, brachiopods, inoceramid bivalves and echinoids. Ammonites are quite common, and are used for zonation. The 'Aucellina Beds', at the base, comprise silty chalks with a fauna dominated by

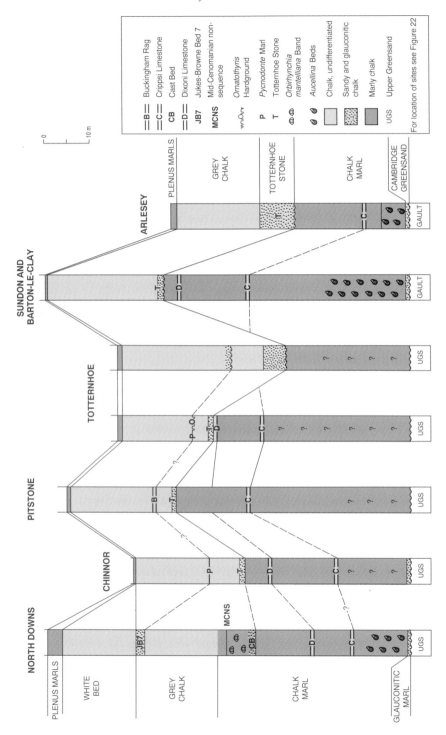

thin-shelled pectinaceans and *Aucellina*. The beds are up to 12 m thick in the North Downs, but increase to 20 m or more in the Chilterns. In the Chilterns, they show well-developed rhythmic bedding, and this also occurs in the overlying beds. A typical rhythm consists of a dark grey, bioclastic marl, with a sharp, burrowed base, which passes up into paler, less argillaceous chalk, and culminates in a spongiferous limestone. The rhythms can be traced from England to the Paris Basin and to Germany. Their origin has been attributed to climatic changes resulting from periodic variations in the orbit of the earth (Milankovitch cycles); they may reflect precessional cycles of approximately 20 000 years duration. Oxygen isotope analyses have shown that the marls correspond to periods of cooler sea-water temperatures, while the paler limestones reflect warmer phases.

Several of the fossiliferous limestones which mark the tops of rhythms can be recognised throughout much of the region (Figure 23). A thick, burrowed limestone in the *Mantelliceras mantelli* Zone, not far above the Aucellina Beds, known as the Crippsi Limestone, contains abundant *Schloenbachia varians* (J Sowerby) and subordinate *Inoceramus crippsi* Mantell. In the lower part of the *Mantelliceras dixoni* Zone, a pair of limestones with common *Inoceramus virgatus* Schlüter comprise the Dixoni Limestone. Higher in the succession, not far above the base of the *Acanthoceras rhotomagense* Zone, a prominent limestone with *Inoceramus tenuis* Mantell and the earliest *Acanthoceras*, is overlain by the Cast Bed, comprising brown, silty chalk with abundant, composite moulds ('casts') of gastropods and other molluscs, small brachiopods, notably *Modestella geinitzii* (Schloenbach), and rare specimens of the belemnite *Actinocamax primus* Arkhangelsky.

In the North Downs, the Cast Bed is overlain by a succession of marl–limestone rhythms with common rhynchonellid brachiopods (the Orbirhynchia mantelliana Band) and, at the top, a limestone with abundant *Sciponoceras*. Above this limestone, there is a change to purer chalks, accompanied by a sudden increase in the ratio of planktonic to benthonic foraminifera, marking the 'p/b' break or mid-Cenomanian non-sequence. The boundary between the Chalk Marl and the Grey Chalk lies a few metres higher.

In the later part of Early Cenomanian times, a fall in sea level resulted in erosion. This is weakly represented in the North Downs where, in the Blue Bell Hill Quarries near Chatham, the Cast Bed is calcarenitic with a somewhat erosional base. Erosion was more marked in the Chilterns and substantial thicknesses of Chalk Marl were removed, so that locally, only the lower part of the *Mantelliceras mantelli* Zone remains (Table 7; Figure 23). The eroded Chalk Marl is overlain by the **Totternhoe Stone**. This takes its name from a village near Dunstable, where the bed, up to 6.5m thick, has been worked as a building stone. It is a brownish grey, bioclastic calcarenite, made up largely of comminuted prisms of inoceramid bivalve shells, with a basal lag of glauconitised and phosphatised chalk pebbles (Table 7; Figure 23). It is highly condensed, incorporating fossils derived from the Cast Bed and Orbirhynchia mantelliana Band. At Houghton Regis, it contains well-

Figure 23 Stratigraphy and correlation of the Lower Chalk of the region, based on quarries and boreholes, supplemented by outcrop data. For location of sections, see Figure 22.

preserved, phosphatised ammonites including *Cunningtoniceras, Schloenbachia coupei* Brongniart and *Turrilites costatus* Lamarck, as well as the belemnite *Actinocamax primus*.

The **Grey Chalk** is less argillaceous, and more massive than the Chalk Marl, and the sedimentary rhythms are less well developed. It is also generally much less fossiliferous, although the terebratulid brachiopod *Concinnithyris subundata* (J Sowerby) is relatively common near the base. In the North Downs, the top of the Grey Chalk is marked by a unit traditionally known as Jukes-Browne Bed 7, which comprises some 2m of bioclastic chalk with cal-carenite-filled, scour-like structures. It yields large specimens of the zonal ammonite *Acanthoceras jukesbrownei* (Spath) and the more marly basal part is characterised by a concentration of small oysters (*Pycnodonte*).

In the Chilterns, the Grey Chalk rests on the Totternhoe Stone. Jukes-Browne Bed 7 may be represented by the 'Buckinghamshire Rag', a lenticular calcarenite, rich in pelletal phosphate and small fish teeth, with glauconitised and phosphatised chalk pebbles. It has been recorded at Butler's Cross near Wendover (Figure 22), and is also present at Pitstone farther north-east. It probably marks a significant non-sequence. At places, including Totternhoe and Hitchin, it is represented by a glauconitised hardground, with common specimens of the thick-shelled terebratulid brachiopod *Ornatothyris sulcifera* (Morris); this is overlain by a thin marl with small *Pycnodonte* and crushed *Inoceramus pictus* J de C Sowerby. The overlying beds comprise massive, off-white chalks, with irregular curvilinear jointing. The equivalent unit in the North Downs, the **White Bed**, is an extremely soft, smooth, white chalk with prismatic jointing, and is known to the quarry workers as 'soapstone'. It contains few fossils, apart from sporadic concentrations of the oyster *Amphi-donte*, sparse *Inoceramus pictus* and crushed thin-shelled echinoids.

The **Plenus Marls** comprise alternating, slightly greenish grey, marls and marly limestones, resting with marked colour contrast on the eroded and burrowed surface of the White Bed or Grey Chalk. Locally, this 'sub-Plenus' erosion surface cuts deeply into these underlying beds (Table 7). The Plenus Marls are more fossiliferous than the beds below, and take their name from the belemnite *Actinocamax plenus* (Blainville) (Plate 13:6), which occurs in the upper part. A standard succession of beds (numbered 1 to 8 from the base) has been recognised within the Plenus Marls throughout southern England and northern France, although at many localities, the succession is incomplete due to non-sequences. In the North Downs, the Plenus Marls are typically about 3 m thick, but in the Chilterns the sequence is relatively condensed, and varies from 0.9 to 1.7 m in thickness. From Hitchin eastwards, *Ornatothyris* becomes a characteristic element of the fauna, and Bed 3 is locally so intensely indurated that it resembles the overlying Melbourn Rock.

MIDDLE AND UPPER CHALK

The succession of white chalk comprising the upper part of the Chalk Group, was originally divided into Middle and Upper Chalk, by recognition of the distinctive Chalk Rock. This defines the base of the Upper Chalk, throughout the Marlborough and Berkshire Downs, and in the Chiltern Hills. However, in the North Downs (and elsewhere in southern England), the Chalk Rock is absent. In these areas, the base of the Upper Chalk has generally been defined at the base of the *Sternotaxis plana* Zone, but this horizon may be difficult to recognise. In order to use a standard definition for the whole region, in this account the base of the Upper Chalk is taken at the incoming of indurated or nodular chalks above the Middle Chalk. This corresponds with the base of the Chalk Rock where it is present, and with the base of the Lewes Chalk elsewhere (Table 7). Principally because of lateral changes in the development of the Chalk Rock (see below), the base of the Upper Chalk is diachronous.

The Middle and Upper Chalk of the Sussex and Kent coasts have been divided into several members (of which the Lewes Chalk is one). They are differentiated by gross lithology, in particular the presence or absence of nodular fabric, flints and marl seams. The members can be recognised in the North Downs (Table 7), but have not yet been applied to the somewhat modified succession in the north-western part of the region.

In several cases, the bases of the members are defined by marl seams which, although generally no more than a few centimetres thick, are conspicuous in exposures. Such marl seams are particularly characteristic of the thicker, basinal successions; they may result from an increased supply of detrital material at times of falling sea level, but some workers consider that they represent contemporaneous volcanic ash falls. They produce distinctive peaks in geophysical logs of boreholes and so are of great value in correlation.

The nodular fabric that characterises some of the members is caused by cementation of the chalk between burrows. In some cases, winnowing of the nodules by currents resulted in pebbly intraformational conglomerates. During prolonged breaks in sedimentation, cementation progressively converted the nodular chalk into a more or less homogeneous chalkstone. The resultant hardground provided a solid substrate for encrusting and boring organisms and, in places, mineralisation has produced pyrite (generally oxidised to yellowish brown limonite in exposures), green glauconite and brown phosphate. Like the marl seams, these hardgrounds are valuable in correlation but, in contrast, they characterise the more condensed successions. They grade basinwards into increasingly poorly defined nodular chalks and finally into an 'omission surface', which may be almost imperceptible apart from a slight yellow or orange coloration from iron minerals. A classic example of this transition is the passage of the Chalk Rock hardground complex into correlative nodular chalks in the North Downs (Table 7; Figure 24).

The high-carbonate chalks of the Middle Chalk and, particularly, the Upper Chalk, are characterised by the development of flint, a form of translucent, grey or black silica. Beds of flint nodules occur at regular intervals related to sedimentary rhythms, and some provide widespread marker-horizons. The flints formed at an early stage of diagenesis, though at some depth below the sea floor. They were originally precipitated as cristobalite which, on deep burial, was altered to microcrystalline quartz. The silica was derived from the skeletons of sponges, radiolarians and diatoms, which dissolved in the generally alkaline environment on burial. Oxidation of hydrogen sulphide, derived from decomposing organic matter, gave rise to localised acidic conditions in which the silica was reprecipitated, replacing calcium carbonate which went into solution. This process occurred preferen-

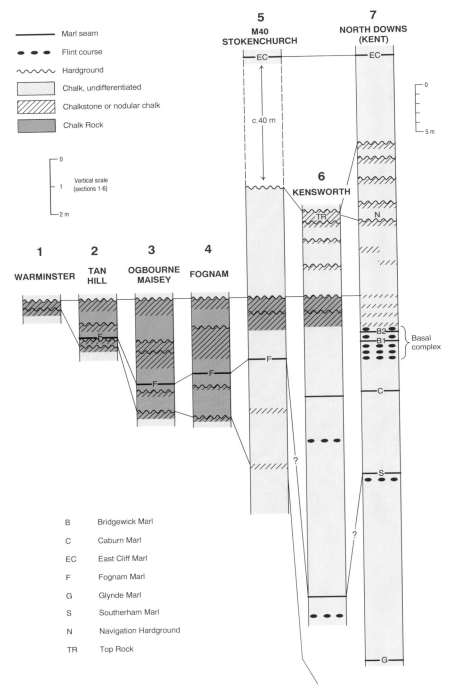

Marl seam
Flint course
Hardground
Chalk, undifferentiated
Chalkstone or nodular chalk
Chalk Rock

Vertical scale
(sections 1-6)

5
M40
STOKENCHURCH

7
NORTH DOWNS
(KENT)

EC

c.40 m

6
KENSWORTH

TR

N

1
WARMINSTER

2
TAN HILL

3
OGBOURNE MAISEY

4
FOGNAM

F

F

F

F

Basal complex

B2
B1

C

S

?

?

?

G

B   Bridgewick Marl

C   Caburn Marl

EC   East Cliff Marl

F   Fognam Marl

G   Glynde Marl

S   Southerham Marl

N   Navigation Hardground

TR   Top Rock

tially in more permeable parts of the sediment, such as burrow-fills. Consequently, the majority of flints are replacements of the chalk in and around burrows (particularly *Thalassinoides*) and their shape reflects the original burrow morphology. In some cases, annular flints formed around burrows; an extreme example is provided by the paramoudra, a vertical flint up to several metres long, formed around the tiny burrow-trace *Bathichnus*. Flint may also occur as sheets, lining fractures both at high angles or roughly parallel to the bedding.

Middle Chalk

The Middle Chalk is 65 to 70 m thick in the North Downs and northern Chilterns, but it thins to only about as 40 m in the Marlborough Downs; this variation is principally due to the diachronous base of the overlying Upper Chalk (Table 7).

The **Holywell Nodular Chalk**, at the base, can be recognised throughout the region. It corresponds approximately to the *Mytiloides* spp. Zone together with the thin underlying *Neocardioceras juddi* Zone. In the North Downs, it was formerly known as the 'Grit Bed' or 'Melbourn Rock Beds'. It is about 10m thick, and is highly condensed relative to the type succession in Sussex, which is about 40m thick. The lower part comprises hard, nodular and pebbly chalk, equating with the Melbourn Rock of the Chilterns (see below); the upper part is coarsely bioclastic, with abundant inoceramid shell debris (*Mytiloides* spp.; Plate 13:4).

In the north-western outcrops of the region, the base of the Middle Chalk is marked by the feature-forming **Melbourn Rock**, named after a village north-east of Royston (Figure 22). It comprises 3 to 4 m of intensely hard, weakly nodular and marl-streaked chalkstones, overlain by coarser-grained, slightly shelly but still relatively indurated chalks. The basal part of the Melbourn Rock is of latest Cenomanian age, and the higher part is Turonian (Table 7). The Melbourn Rock is overlain by *Mytiloides*-rich shell-detrital chalks corresponding with the upper part of the Holywell Nodular Chalk of the North Downs. North-eastwards from Dunstable, the first flints occur in the uppermost part of this unit, but in the southern Chilterns, only the very highest beds of the Middle Chalk contain flints.

Above the Holywell Nodular Chalk, the **New Pit Chalk** of the North Downs extends into the lower part of the *Terebratulina lata* Zone. It is characterised by softer, smooth, massively bedded chalk with marl seams and, near the base, rare flints. It is relatively poorly fossiliferous apart from *Inoceramus cuvieri* J Sowerby and *Terebratulina lata* (Etheridge). In the eastern part of the North Downs, the lower part of the New Pit Chalk is nodular and pebbly, and these beds, together with the underlying Holywell Nodular Chalk, have been termed the Shakespeare Cliff Member.

In the north-western outcrops of the region, smooth chalk like that of the New Pit Chalk, extend up into the higher part of the *lata* Zone. A quarry in

Figure 24 Diagrammatic sections illustrating the eastward passage of the Chalk Rock complex into correlative nodular beds of the Lewes Chalk. Note reduced scale of section 7 (North Downs, Kent). For location of sections, see Figure 22.

these beds near Great Chesterford, on the northern margin of the region, is famous for its superbly preserved fossils, including early forms of *Echinocorys, Micraster corbovis* Forbes and *Inoceramus lamarcki* Parkinson. Two marl seams seen both here and at Kensworth Quarry, near Dunstable, equate with the Southerham and Caburn Marls of the North Downs, which there lie within the basal part of the Upper Chalk.

Upper Chalk

Compared with the succession elsewhere in southern England, the Upper Chalk succession within the region is thin, because it is condensed over the London Platform, and also because the youngest beds have been removed by post-Cretaceous erosion. A maximum of 100m or so of Upper Chalk is preserved beneath the basal Palaeogene unconformity. The highest preserved Chalk generally belongs to the *Micraster coranguinum* Zone, but the succession locally extends upwards into the *Offaster pilula* Zone (Table 7).

In the Marlborough and Berkshire Downs, and in the Chilterns, the base of the Upper Chalk is marked by the **Chalk Rock**, a sequence of glauconitised hardgrounds and chalkstones. This is a condensed sequence representing the higher part of the *lata* Zone and the lower part of the *S. plana* Zone (Table 7). In its most extreme development, to the south-west of the region near Warminster in Wiltshire, the Chalk Rock is represented by a unit of welded hardgrounds only 1m thick, which corresponds to beds which are perhaps 40 m thick in the North Downs (Figure 24).

In its type area of the Marlborough Downs, the Chalk Rock is 4 to 5 m thick, and seven separate hardgrounds have been recognised. The highest (Hitch Wood) hardground of this complex, yields a diverse fauna of gastropods and ammonites, including the heteromorph *Hyphantoceras reussianum* (d'Orbigny) (Plate 13:5), preserved as moulds. Near the base, the Chalk Rock includes the Fognam Marl, which probably equates with the Southerham Marl of the North Downs. Eastwards from the Marlborough Downs, the hardgrounds below the Fognam Marl pass into nodular chalks. The overlying condensed beds form the Chalk Rock of the southern Chilterns (the Henley Rock of earlier literature). It is about 1m thick, and is exposed in the M40 motorway cutting near Stokenchurch. Around Dunstable, in the northern Chilterns, the Chalk Rock is represented only by the Hitch Wood Hardground and its overlying pebble bed. At Kensworth Quarry, and at its type locality south of Hitchin, the hard ground has yielded well-preserved, phosphatised, internal moulds of ammonites, and other fossils of the '*reussianum* fauna'. Near Baldock, east of Hitchin, the pebble bed passes abruptly into weakly glauconitised and phosphatised, highly fossiliferous, nodular chalks.

In the North Downs, the Chalk Rock, as described above, is not developed. In its absence, the base of the Upper Chalk is conveniently drawn at the base of the **Lewes Chalk**. This is characterised by fossiliferous nodular chalk with hardgrounds, which contrasts markedly with the smooth, uniform chalk of the underlying New Pit Chalk. It contains regular courses of flint nodules, and a number of marl seams, including the Glynde Marls at the base, and the Southerham and Caburn Marls in the highest part of the *lata* Zone.

Above the Caburn Marl, a thin succession of closely spaced marl seams, associated with large, nodular flints constitutes the 'Basal Complex' (Figures

24 and 25) at the base of the *S. plana* Zone, which has been used to define the base of the Upper Chalk in some previous accounts. The overlying nodular chalks yield the distinctive '*reussianum* fauna' characteristic of the topmost Chalk Rock elsewhere.

The upper part of the Lewes Chalk of the North Downs contains a number of hardgrounds, mainly within the lower part of the *Micraster cortestudinarium* Zone (Figure 25). The sequence is further condensed in the Chilterns, where the corresponding strata are capped by a thin chalkstone, known as the Top Rock, about 4 m above the Chalk Rock (Figure 24). At Kensworth (Figure 24) and elsewhere, several weakly mineralised hardgrounds are developed below the Top Rock. In places, the Top Rock yields a rich fauna of early Coniacian inoceramids, including *Inoceramus waltersdorfensis* (Andert) and *I. rotundatus* Fiege, notably at Redbournbury Quarry, north-west of St Albans. Its upper surface is a glauconitised hardground overlain by dark green, glauconitised chalk pebbles, including reworked sponges and *Micraster cortestudinarium* (Goldfuss).

Above the hardgrounds in the North Downs, the topmost part of the Lewes Chalk (the youngest part of the *cortestudinarium* Zone) comprises a few metres of somewhat nodular chalk, which is generally capped by the East Cliff Marl. At Rochester and some other localities such as the Rose and Crown Pit near Warlingham, the marl is absent and the Rochester Hardground is developed (Figure 25). In the Chilterns, the equivalent beds are much thicker, massive chalks; in the M40 motorway cutting near Stokenchurch, the East Cliff Marl lies some 40 m above the Top Rock.

In the North Downs, the Lewes Chalk is overlain by the **Seaford Chalk**, which corresponds approximately to the *Micraster coranguinum* Zone. It is characterised by soft, white, non-nodular chalk with regularly spaced bands of large nodular flints and conspicuous beds of inoceramid shell fragments at some horizons. It includes several important flint marker beds. One, known as Bedwell's Columnar Flint Band, is characterised by paramoudra-like flints, which are well exposed in the quarries between Purfleet and Grays. The top of the Seaford Chalk is marked by the Clandon Hardground (named after a quarry near Guildford), which is the lateral equivalent of the nodular 'Barrois Sponge Bed' of the Isle of Thanet (Table 7; Figure 25).

In the north-western outcrop, equivalent beds of the *coranguinum* Zone can be seen in old quarries in the Colne Valley south of Rickmansworth, at Essendon, west of Hertford, and between Hertford and Ware (Figure 22). Generally, the highest part of the zone is missing in this part of the region, but the Clandon Hardground is found at Taplow, where it forms a base to a phosphatic chalk succession (see below). South of Newbury, the Clandon Hardground probably passes into the Whitway Rock which contains the same form of *Echinocorys* as the Barrois Sponge Bed.

The youngest chalk exposed in the North Downs, comprising the **Margate Chalk**, belongs to the *Uintacrinus socialis*, *Marsupites testudinarius* and, locally, the basal part of the *Offaster pilula* zones (Table 7). It contains few flints and lacks the marl seams characteristic of the correlative Newhaven Chalk of Sussex. Beds of the *socialis* and *testudinarius* zones can also be seen in old quarries at Sudbury, in the north-east. The youngest exposed chalk of the region belongs to the lower part of the *pilula* Zone, and is found at Kintbury and Winterbourne near Newbury, and also near Taplow. At Kintbury, the *socialis* to *pilula* zones are characterised by normal white chalk. However, at both Winterbourne and Taplow,

Chalk, undifferentiated	Ca	Caburn Marl
Chalkstone or nodular chalk	EC	East Cliff Marl
Hardground	G	Glynde Marl
C Clandon	S	Southerham Marl
N Navigation	•••	Flint course
R Rochester	BC	Bedwell's Columnar
Marl seam	ECST	East Cliff Semitabular
B Bridgewick Marl	W3	Whitaker's 3-inch

BSB	Barrois Sponge Bed
⌣ ⌣	*Cladoceramus*-rich bed
P	Palaeogene deposits

equivalent beds include brown, phosphatic chalks, which accumulated in small, structurally controlled, erosional troughs. At Taplow, the phosphatic chalk occurs in two main beds, 1.2 m and 2.4 m thick, each with a basal layer of phosphatised chalk pebbles. The lower bed rests on the phosphatised Clandon Hardground. These beds are very fossiliferous, being particularly rich in belemnites; the lower bed yields *Actinocamax verus* Miller together with *Uintacrinus socialis* Grinnell, and the upper *Gonioteuthis granulata* (Blainville).

Figure 25 Simplified stratigraphy, zonation and correlation of key outcrop and borehole successions of the Upper Chalk in the southern part of the region, using the Dover–Thanet succession as a standard. See Figure 22 for locations.

8   Palaeogene and Neogene

At the end of the Cretaceous Period, many types of plants and animals which had characterised the Mesozoic Era became extinct, and different groups of fossils are found in younger strata. For this reason, the post-Cretaceous era, commencing with the Palaeogene Period, is named the Cainozoic (from the Greek 'new life') (Table 1). The term 'Tertiary' (third age) is also used for the Palaeogene to Neogene interval. In recent years, the cause of this major extinction has been sought in some kind of sudden catastrophe; for example, a major meteorite impact has been suggested to explain the disappearance of the dinosaurs at this time. However, for many Mesozoic groups, including the ammonites, belemnites, inoceramid and rudist bivalves, their decline and eventual disappearance seems to have taken place over a period of millions of years. The latest Cretaceous and earliest Palaeogene periods were times of increased tectonic and volcanic activity, accompanied by a global fall in sea level, a concomitant increase in land area, and a cooling of the climate. This changing environment undoubtedly led to the demise of many forms of life, and the evolutionary development of others. Thus, it may be unnecessary to invoke cosmic disasters to explain the extinction of the dinosaurs, although such an event may have hastened their departure.

The beginning of the Palaeogene Period saw profound changes in the physiography of Europe. A phase of crustal compression associated with the building of the Alps in southern Europe, may have begun at this time. It ultimately caused the 'inversion' of Mesozoic structures, during which the Wessex Basin and the East Midlands Shelf were gradually uplifted with the formation of structures such as the Weald Anticline, while the London Platform subsided, and the syncline of the London Basin began to develop. Falling sea level caused the emergence of large areas of land, and in the London and Thames Valley region, a considerable thickness of Upper Chalk was eroded away. Further crustal compression occurred in later Palaeogene times, and culminated in the early Neogene (Miocene), by which time the London Basin had assumed the synclinal form we see today (Figures 1, 2 and 26).

PALAEOGENE

During Palaeogene times, the region became an area of sedimentation within which up to 320 m of strata, of Palaeocene and Eocene age, were laid down (Table 8). They include shallow marine, coastal and fluvial sediments, which were the subject of intense study by geologists in the nineteenth century, not least because of their rich and varied fossil faunas (Plate 14). This early work

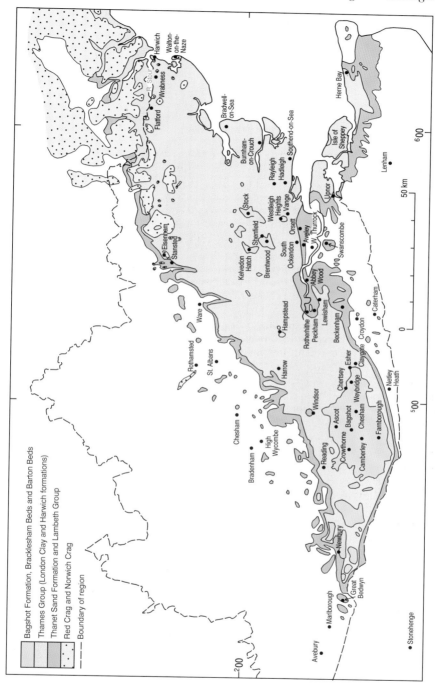

Bagshot Formation, Bracklesham Beds and Barton Beds

Thames Group (London Clay and Harwich formations)

Thanet Sand Formation and Lambeth Group

Red Crag and Norwich Crag

Boundary of region

Figure 26 Outcrop of Palaeogene and Neogene strata and locality sketch map.

Table 8   Main stratal subdivisions of the Palaeogene and Neogene succession in the region.

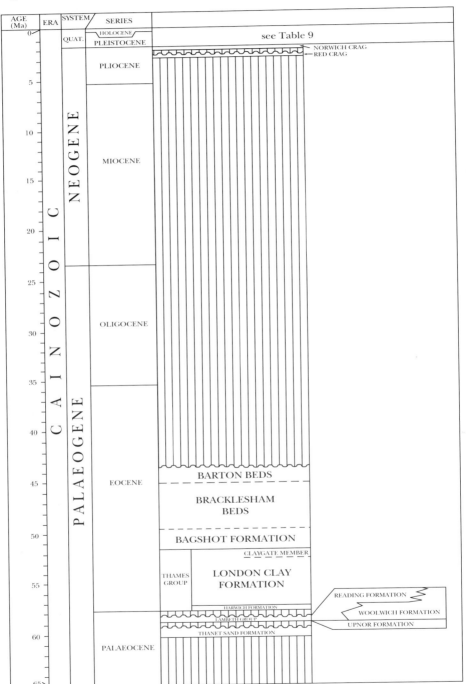

established the basic stratigraphical framework although, in many cases, the age relationships of the different units were far from clear. In the North Sea Basin, deeper-water Palaeogene deposits are up to 2 km thick, and include sands which form important oil and gas reservoirs. This economic aspect has given a new stimulus to geological research in the London Basin, leading to clarification of the relationships of the various units, and has necessitated some revision of the traditional nomenclature.

Historically, assemblages of fossils such as bivalves (Plate 14), benthonic foraminifera and ostracods have been used as the main tool for biostratigraphical correlation. More recently, planktonic foraminifera, calcareous nannoplankton (similar to the coccolithophorids of the Chalk), and dinoflagellates have been used. Of greatest potential for correlation are spores derived from land vegetation, because they are found in both nonmarine and marine sediments.

The Palaeogene fossil mammal fauna is less important for correlation, but nevertheless provides a fascinating insight into evolutionary trends following the extinction of the dinosaurs. Bones and teeth have been collected from the basal beds of the London Clay at Harwich, and there is an important site in the Blackheath Beds at Abbey Wood, in south-east London. In addition, fossil shark teeth are commonly seen in all the marine Palaeogene strata, and may be concentrated at some horizons by reworking and winnowing.

A useful means of correlation is provided by magnetostratigraphy. This technique utilises the remanent magnetism in grains of haematite within sediments, to identify the periodic reversals of the earth's magnetic field. A standard correlation of magnetic anomalies and calcareous nannofossil zones is now established in deep-water successions where there was more or less continuous deposition throughout the Palaeogene. Comparative studies in the London Basin have shown that the sedimentary succession there is relatively incomplete (Table 8). Volcanic ash (tuff or tephra) beds are also valuable for correlation within the early Palaeogene succession. Fine-grained volcanic ash, from explosive eruptions in the North Atlantic, was carried by the wind and deposited over large areas. Ash beds are readily recognised in deeper water sediments, but within shallow–water sediments which characterise much of the succession in the London Basin, the ash was generally reworked and mixed with other material, so that the beds are not well defined. Radiometric dating of sedimentary glauconite grains, using the potassium-argon and rubidium-strontium methods, has also been applied, but has not yielded entirely consistent results. Studies of stable carbon isotopes, present in fossil shells, plant debris and soil horizons, holds some promise for the future as a means of indirect dating of the sequence.

Thanet Sand Formation

The oldest Palaeogene deposit, the Thanet Sand Formation, is found only in the south-eastern part of the region, with the principal outcrops occurring in south-east London and north Kent. The formation is thickest beneath the Thames Estuary, where up to 32 m are present (Figure 27). To the west of the main outcrop, it is preserved locally in solution pipes in the Chalk of the

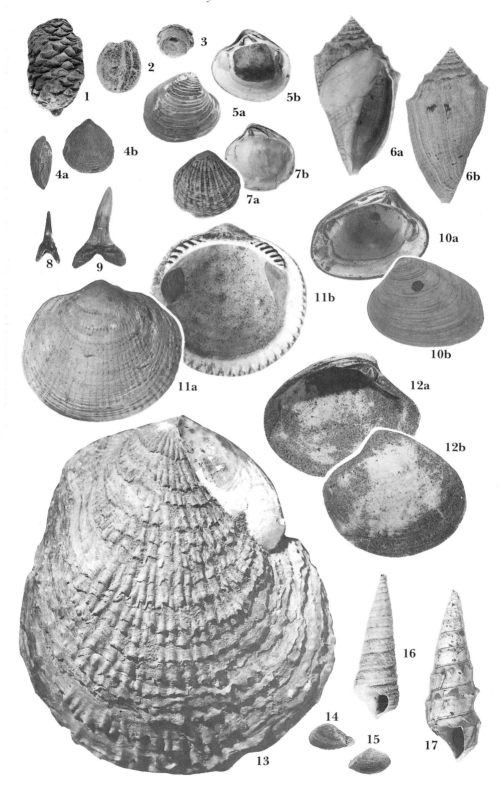

North Downs, indicating that the formation was originally far more extensive.

At the base, the 'Bullhead Bed' rests unconformably on the Chalk (Plate 15). Up to 0.5 m thick, it is a conglomerate containing rounded flint pebbles, and large, almost unworn nodular flints ('bullheads'). The flints are typically coated with dark green glauconite, and lie within a matrix of glauconitic sandy clay.

The bulk of the Thanet Sand consists of silty, fine-grained sand which tends to be clayey and more silty in the lower part. The sediments are characteristically bioturbated, so that primary sedimentary structures, such as lamination, are generally lacking. The colour varies between greenish and brownish grey, depending on the amount of glauconite present, but at the surface the sands weather to a pale yellowish grey. Analyses of 'heavy mineral' grains (such as epidote, garnet, kyanite, and staurolite) indicate that the sands were probably derived from the metamorphic rocks of the Scottish Highlands, and were transported southwards by longshore drift. There was also some input from contemporary volcanic ash-falls.

Macrofossils found in the Thanet Sand include the bivalves *Arctica morrisi* (J de C Sowerby) (Plate 14:12), *Corbula regulbiensis* Morris (Plate 14:14), *Nemocardium semigranulatum* (J Sowerby) and *Pholadomya konincki* Nyst, and the gastropod *Aporrhais sowerbyi* (Fleming). Microfauna indicates that the greater part of the formation was deposited in a shallow sea, up to 50 m deep, and shows that the climate was generally cool, although warmer conditions prevailed during deposition of the youngest sediments.

Eastwards, the formation generally becomes more clayey, and in some boreholes, for example at Flatford and Bradwell-on-Sea (Figure 26), grey clayey silt and clay are dominant. There, the succession includes a bed of red clay near the base; this is an important marker for correlation with the much thicker Ormesby Clay Formation which replaces the Thanet Sand in Suffolk and Norfolk.

Plate 14 Fossils from the Palaeogene formations (all natural size)

1 *Platycarya richardsonii* (Bowerbank) (catkin); London Clay Formation
2 *Wetherellia variabilis* Bowerbank (fruit); London Clay Formation
3 *Cinnamomum globulare* Reid & Chandler (cinnamon berry); London Clay Formation
4a–b *Terebratulina wardenensis* Elliott; London Clay Formation
5a–b *Astarte rugata* J Sowerby; London Clay Formation
6a–b *Athleta nodosus* (J de C Sowerby); London Clay Formation–Barton Beds
7a–b *Venericardium trinobantium* Wrigley; London Clay Formation–Barton Beds
8–9 Sharks' teeth; Thanet Sand Formation–Barton Beds
10a–b *Astarte tenera* Morris; Thanet Sand Formation
11a–b *Glycymeris plumstediensis* (J Sowerby); Harwich Formation: Blackheath Beds
12a–b *Arctica morrisi* (J de C Sowerby); Thanet Sand Formation–London Clay Formation
13 *Ostrea bellovacina* Lamarck; Thanet Sand Formation–Harwich Formation
14–15 *Corbula regulbiensis* Morris; Thanet Sand Formation–Lambeth Group
16 *Tympanotonus funatus* (J Sowerby); Lambeth Group–Harwich Formation
17 *Brotia melanioides* (J Sowerby); Lambeth Group–Harwich Formation

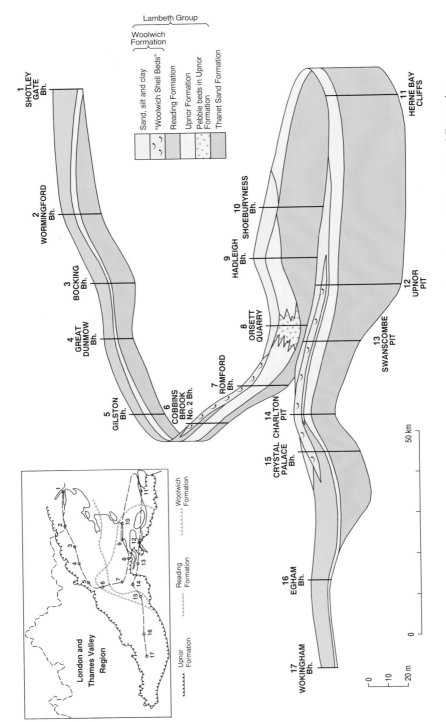

Figure 27 Schematic section illustrating stratigraphy and facies variation in the Lambeth Group and Thanet Sand Formation. Inset shows lateral extent of formations at depth, beneath younger rocks.

Plate 15   Thanet Sand Formation resting upon Upper Chalk, Ballingdon, near Sudbury, Essex (1979). The irregular junction is due to channelling prior to deposition of the Thanet Sand, combined with later solution of the chalk. The rounded flints of the Bullhead Bed, with their characteristic coating of greenish glauconite, can be seen just above the junction. Overlying beds comprise fine-grained, silty sands (A13253).

Lambeth Group

The Lambeth Group comprises the Woolwich and Reading Beds of previous accounts. It has a more extensive distribution than the Thanet Sand Formation, extending to the westernmost part of the London Basin at Newbury (Figures 26 and 27). It is generally 10 to 15 m thick at outcrop and a maximum of 28 m was proved in a borehole at Chertsey.

The basal beds of the Lambeth Group comprise the **Upnor Formation** (formerly the 'Bottom Bed'). It comprises 5 to 6 m of medium-grained sands, which were laid down in a shallow sea which spread across the region following a period of emergence and erosion. A radical change in paleogeography is indicated by the presence of heavy minerals derived from an Armorican province to the south-west, contrasting with the Scottish provenance of the Thanet Sand Formation. Locally, for example in south-east London, the sand is patchily cemented by calcium carbonate into large, irregularly shaped sandstone masses. The beds contain abundant, coarse, well-rounded grains of glauconite; at outcrop, they weather to a pale brown colour, with the glauconite imparting a 'pepper and salt' appearance. Generally, there is a basal conglomeratic layer containing rounded flint pebbles. In the western part of the region, where the formation oversteps the Thanet Sand and rests directly on the Chalk, this basal bed includes unworn, nodular flints, like those found at the base of the Thanet Sand. There, the formation characteristically contains the oyster *Ostrea bellovacina* Lamarck (Plate 14).

In the eastern part of the region, particularly in south-east Essex and north Kent, the basal pebble bed is locally absent, and it is difficult to distinguish the Upnor Formation from the underlying Thanet Sand. In this area, the formation includes coarser sand beds (notably at the base), pale grey clay partings and beds of small, well-rounded, black flints. The sediments are commonly extensively burrowed; cylindrical *Ophiomorpha* burrows, made by a type of shrimp, can be observed in quarries near Orsett, West Thurrock and Swanscombe.

In the north and west of the outcrop, beds of green and red mottled sandy clay occur near the top of the formation, due to weathering associated with the succeeding Reading Formation. This weathering has also resulted in bleached and red-stained flint pebbles, which occur in a bed, 3m thick, at the top of the formation in central and south-east London.

At Orsett (Figure 26), the Upnor Formation includes up to 10m of coarse gravel, composed of well-rounded pebbles of black flint (Plate 16; Figure 27). The pebbles are pitted by 'chatter-marks', formed as they were pounded together in high-energy conditions, and also show smoothly moulded contacts, caused by post-depositional pressure solution. The deposits, formerly thought to be Blackheath Beds, probably represent part of an offshore barrier, or the infill of a tidal channel.

After deposition of the Upnor Formation, a fall in sea level caused the sea to retreat to the east of the region, and fresh- and brackish-water conditions were established across the London Basin. At this time, the broadly equivalent Reading and Woolwich formations were deposited.

The **Reading Formation** is present throughout the western and northern parts of the basin. It is typically some 10 to 15 m thick, but reaches a maximum of about 22 m at Chertsey. It is formed of sediments laid down on marshy mudflats, crossed by river channels. Lithologies are very variable, but generally the formation is dominated by clay, which is characteristically mottled, blotched and spotted in shades of red, brown, purple and grey. This coloration is a result of weathering and soil-formation (pedogenesis), which took place soon after deposition, and indicates a warm climate with a marked dry season. As might be expected, fossils are rare, but thin plant-rich seams and leaf impressions have been found. Relatively unweathered, laminated and bio-turbated silt and fine-grained sand occur locally, particularly in a tract which trends north-east from central London. These beds were laid down in lagoons and remained submerged; they were thus unaffected by pedogenesis. Lenticular bodies of cross-bedded, medium-grained sand, commonly containing layers of intraformational clay-flake conglomerate, also occur. These represent the deposits of river channels which crossed the alluvial mudflats. The best examples occur near Newbury, where the deposits are (exceptionally) up to 10 m thick and, in places, contain concretions cemented by silica and iron.

In the London area, the Reading Formation is replaced by the **Woolwich Formation**, and the two interdigitate in central and south-east London (Figure 27). The Woolwich Formation reaches a maximum thickness of 10 m near Lewisham in south-east London. It includes a variety of lithologies, laid down in a lagoonal or estuarine environment. The most widespread facies

Plate 16   Orsett Depot Quarry, near Grays, Essex (1973). These gravels of well-rounded flint pebbles are a local development in the Upnor Formation, which is more typically developed as medium-grained sands, like those seen in the upper part of the face (A12270).

comprises clay, packed with mollusc shells. These 'Woolwich Shell Beds', generally 1 to 3 m thick, contain a brackish-water fauna including the gastropods *Brotia* and *Tympanotonos*, and the bivalves *Corbicula* and *Ostrea tenera* J Sowerby. Other widespread lithologies include ferruginous sand, lignitic sand, and lignite, which occur at the base of the formation, for example at Aveley and at Upnor (Figure 26). The sands are locally cemented by silica, and may be contemporaneous with the sarsens described below. Also characteristic of the formation, but of more limited distribution, are thinly bedded and laminated, greyish brown, fine-grained sands, and grey silts and clays (formerly referred to as 'Striped Sands' or 'Striped Loams'). These beds overlie the shell beds in south London, and contain a similar, though less abundant, brackish-water fauna. Around Peckham and Rotherhithe, a limestone bed (the 'Paludina Limestone') at the top of the formation, contains the freshwater gastropods *Hydrobia*, *Planorbis* and *Viviparus*, indicating the presence of a freshwater lake. Sandy interbeds containing glauconite grains and a sparse marine fauna, found principally in north Kent and south Essex, indicate rare marine incursions from the east.

Thames Group

After a rise in sea level, shallow marine conditions were established again in the eastern part of the region, and the **Harwich Formation** was deposited. This formation occurs mainly in the east and north-east of the London Basin, and rests disconformably on the Lambeth Group (Figure 28). In south Essex and north Kent, the contact is markedly erosive, and cuts down as far as the Upnor Formation. To the south of Caterham, pebble beds of the Harwich Formation rest directly on Chalk, but these may be out of place, having been transported from their original position by Quaternary solifluxion.

The formation is made up of several distinct facies. In the Lewisham, Beckenham and Croydon area of south London, it consists of cross-bedded

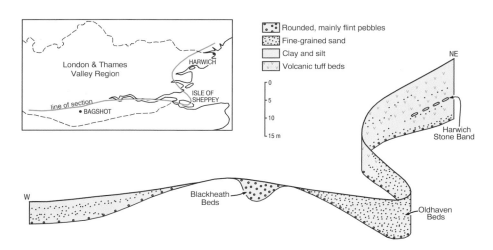

Figure 28   Schematic section illustrating facies variation in the Harwich Formation.

sand with rounded pebbles of black flint. These strata, known as the Black-heath Beds, are up to 12 m thick at Lewisham; they infill channels cut into the Lambeth Group. To the east, in Essex and north Kent, the formation comprises the Oldhaven Beds. These are up to 10 m thick in the Isle of Sheppey, but thin westwards, and are absent in central London. At Upnor and Aveley, the Oldhaven Beds consist of about 2 m of yellow, cross-bedded, shelly sand with a basal pebble bed. The fauna is similar to that of the Woolwich Formation and includes brackish and freshwater fossils indicating an estuarine environment. Marine fossils are also found, particularly in the east and northwards, into Essex, where the beds are replaced by grey to brown, variably glauconitic, clayey and silty fine-grained sand. These strata, up to 17 m thick in boreholes at Bradwell-on-Sea, were formerly included in the London Clay (as the Harwich Member and the 'London Clay Basement Bed'). Characteristically, they contain layers of volcanic ash, which are bluish grey, silty clays when fresh, but weather to pale yellow-brown, as can be seen in the river cliffs of the Stour on the north-eastern boundary of the region, and in quarries around Elsenham, near Stansted. The most prominent ash bed lies within the 'Harwich Stone Band', a sequence of tabular calcareous siltstone concretions, which is exposed on the foreshore at Harwich.

As sea level continued to rise, marine deposition gradually spread westwards across the region from the North Sea, joining with the Hampshire Basin to the south-west. At its maximum extent, the sea may have been up to 200 m deep in the eastern parts of the region.

The **London Clay Formation**, which was deposited at this time, is the most widespread and best known of the English Palaeogene deposits, and accounts for the greater part of the Palaeogene outcrop in the London Basin (Figure 26). It forms an ideal medium for tunnelling, and its presence beneath much of Greater London has facilitated development there. The London Clay is up to 150 m thick in south Essex and north Kent, but thins westwards to about 90 m at Reading, and is only 4.6 m in an outlier at Great Bedwyn in Wiltshire, which probably lay close to the western limit of deposition.

The formation consists mainly of dark bluish to brownish grey clay, containing variable amounts of fine-grained sand and silt; the latter is particularly abundant at the base and top of the formation, and in the west of the region. The clays generally weather to a chocolate-brown colour, and the more sandy beds to an orange shade. Clay minerals present include illite, kaolinite and smectite. The presence of smectite has an important effect on the engineering properties of the London Clay, rendering it particularly susceptible to heave caused by alternate wetting and drying near the surface. Beds of calcareous 'cementstone' concretions, up to 0.4 m in diameter, occur sporadically; some are septarian, with calcite veins. Phosphatic nodules, barite and siderite also occur, and glauconite, in the form of small pellets and microcrystalline grains, is quite common in some of the more sandy beds. Pyrite occurs disseminated throughout the sediment, as a replacement of fossil shell debris, and as nodules up to 30 mm in diameter. Its breakdown in the weathered zone gives rise to crystals of selenite (calcium sulphate).

Five sedimentary cycles (Units A to E) have been recognised within the London Clay, each recording an initial transgression, followed by gradual shallowing of the sea. A typical cycle commences with a bed containing scattered glauconite grains and, in some cases, a few rounded flint pebbles.

This is followed by a sequence of clays, which become progressively more silty and sandy upwards. These cycles can be most clearly recognised in the west, where the sea was shallower; the glauconitic marker beds at the base of each cycle die out towards the east.

The distribution of macrofossils in the London Clay is largely facies-controlled, but several mollusc species have relatively short ranges, including the bivalve *Corbula globosa* J Sowerby, which is dominant in the middle and upper part of the formation. In addition, in the east of the region, the crinoid *Balanocrinus subbasaltiformis* (Miller) is restricted to the middle of Unit B and the brachiopod *Terebratulina wardenensis* Elliott (Plate 14:4) is recorded only from the lower parts of units C and D. In general, molluscs are relatively common at the top and base of the London Clay, and are often particularly well preserved in cementstone nodules. Microfossils include diatoms and arenaceous foraminifera, which are most common near the base; an abundant and diverse fauna of foraminifera and ostracods occurs in the middle part.

Many fossil seeds and fruits of land plants have been collected from the London Clay, notably from the coastal exposures at Burnham-on-Crouch, Wrabness, Harwich, Walton-on-the-Naze and especially from the Isle of Sheppey, where landslips washed by waves constantly release new material. The vegetation was probably transported to the coast by rivers, as large floating masses, which drifted far out into the sea. The fossils are generally preserved in pyrite, and may retain delicate cellular detail, but at some localities, for example Walton-on-the-Naze and South Ockendon, the flora is preserved as carbonaceous material. Some 500 different plant species have been described, including mangroves, palms and more familiar types such as magnolia, dogwoods, laurel, cinnamon and bay (Plate 14). These give a picture of a landscape covered by a tropical rain-forest, and bordered by a swampy coastal plain. Remains of land vertebrates may also be found, and the succession at Walton-on-the-Naze has yielded an important collection of fossil birds.

The youngest part of the London Clay Formation, corresponding with the upper part of Unit E, is known as the **Claygate Member**. This forms a transition between the deep-water, dominantly argillaceous London Clay, and the succeeding shallow-water, arenaceous Bagshot Formation. The member occurs widely in Surrey, where it comprises well-laminated, orange sands interbedded with pale grey to lilac clays, some 15 m thick at Claygate, near Esher. These sediments probably accumulated in a zone of fluctuating slack-water and turbulent conditions, in water depths of between 20 and 40 m. The Claygate Member also occurs as outliers in Essex, where it reaches its maximum thickness of 20 m. The lower beds are dominantly clay and sandy clay with some sand bodies. Generally (for example at Shenfield, Vange, Rayleigh and Hadleigh), the upper beds are laminated sands and clays like those of the type area in Surrey, but at Kelvedon Hatch, Brentwood and Stock, these beds are replaced by silts and fine-grained sands. The fauna, particularly from Essex, includes molluscs which also occur in the upper sandy part of the London Clay; the bivalve *Venericardia trinobantium* Wrigley (Plate 14:7) however, is apparently restricted to the Claygate Member. The brachiopod *Lingula* is common in the upper part of the sequence and, because it has a chitinous shell, may be found in weathered beds.

Bagshot Formation

The strata overlying the London Clay Formation in the London Basin, were formerly known as the Lower, Middle and Upper Bagshot Beds. In this account, these units are classified respectively as Bagshot Formation, Bracklesham Beds and Barton Beds, because of their probable equivalence to those units in the Hampshire Basin (Table 8). However, the terminology of these beds should be regarded as provisional until a more definite correlation is established.

There was a shallowing of the sea after deposition of the London Clay and the Bagshot Formation was laid down in a shallow-marine, or possibly estuarine, environment. The main outcrop of the formation is centred on Bagshot Heath, near Camberley (Figure 26). Outliers occur in the Newbury area to the west, at Harrow and Hampstead north of London and also in south Essex, notably at Brentwood and Rayleigh. The succession shows evidence of repeated periods of aggradation and erosion. It is dominated by orange or pale yellow, fine-grained sand, with thin beds of pale grey clay. The thicker sand beds generally show cross-bedding. Lignitic clay horizons with comminuted plant debris have been recorded in the west, for example in the Enborne valley, near Newbury. Greenish grey clays and brown silts also occur in this area, and pebble beds are common in the lower part of the formation. Pebble beds containing rounded, black flints (the 'Bagshot Pebble Bed') have also been recorded at Langtons, near Brentwood, in Essex. Elsewhere on the outcrop in Essex, superficially similar pebbly sands may be younger, perhaps Quaternary in age.

The Bagshot Formation is very variable in thickness. In the Bagshot–Chertsey area, it is probably up to 40 m thick, although the upper boundary with the overlying Bracklesham Beds is commonly difficult to define. At Ascot, just to the north, the thickness is reduced to only 7 m. In Essex, where the top of the formation is absent due to erosion, a maximum of 27 m was penetrated in a borehole at Stock. The formation overlies the London Clay conformably throughout the region, generally resting on the Claygate Member. The absence of the latter in the westernmost part of the region may be due to lateral passage into the lower part of the Bagshot Formation, suggesting that the base of the Bagshot Formation is diachronous, becoming younger to the east.

The fauna of the Bagshot Formation is sparse, probably in part due to decalcification. However, examples of marine mollusca, including the gastropod *Ringicula*, have been recovered as limonitic casts from a borehole at Westley Heights in Essex, and the bivalve *Venericor planicosta* (Lamarck) has been recorded in a calcareous bed near Newbury.

Bracklesham Beds

The Bracklesham Beds overlie the Bagshot Formation to the south-west of London, notably at St George's Hill near Weybridge, and in the Chobham, Crowthorne and Farnborough areas (Figure 26). Their thickness varies from 12 to 30 m. The strata are of variable character, and include interbedded, greenish grey, glauconitic sand, yellowish brown, sandy clay, and pale grey to lilac or bluish grey clay. Cross-bedded, pebbly units also occur, particularly in the upper part of the sequence, and ironstones are present locally. Near Chobham, glauconitic sands interbedded with laminated clays have yielded many fossils, mainly fish teeth and casts of shells; these indicate deposition in a warm, shallow-marine environment. The discovery of the large, chambered foraminifer *Nummulites laevigatus* (Bruguirè) implies correlation with the middle part (Earnley Formation) of the Bracklesham Beds of the Hampshire Basin.

Barton Beds

The Barton Beds, restricted to the Chobham and Bagshot areas of Surrey, are dominated by yellowish brown, fine-grained sands, locally glauconitic in the lowest part, with subordinate silt beds and clay partings. A maximum thickness of 70 m has been recorded at Bagshot but the full sequence is not preserved due to erosion. At the base, an impersistent bed up to 3.5 m thick contains rounded flint and chert pebbles; the presence of chert indicates that by this time, denudation had uncovered the Lower Greensand, probably in the western Weald.

The Barton Beds contain a sparse marine fauna, preserved as ferruginous shell casts. Although a few species are diagnostic of the Barton Beds, other forms range upwards from the Bracklesham Beds.

Sarsens

Sporadic blocks of indurated sandstone, known as sarsens, are found on the Chalk outcrop of the Marlborough and Berkshire Downs, the Chiltern Hills, and also on the North Downs of Kent. They are commonly found in association with, or embedded in, deposits of Clay-with-Flints (see Chapter 9). The best known examples are those used in the megalithic monuments such as Stonehenge and Avebury. Old accounts suggest that sarsens were formerly more widespread, many having been broken up to provide stone for buildings and roads. However, abundant sarsens in their natural state, some several metres in diameter, can still be seen in a few places, for example at Fyfield Down, between Marlborough and Avebury (Plate 17). Sarsens are generally white or pale grey, very pure, fine-grained, quartz sandstones, with a siliceous cement. Traces of rootlets are quite common. These sarsens probably represent outlying fluvial sand deposits of the Reading and Woolwich formations. They indicate that Palaeogene strata formerly extended well beyond their present outcrop, and may originally have covered most of the region, and indeed much of southern England. Blocks of sarsen sandstone are also known from the heathlands of Surrey; these probably formed within the younger Barton Beds.

Also included in the general category of sarsens, are silicified flint conglomerates, such as the Hertfordshire Puddingstone. This typically consists of well-rounded flint pebbles in a matrix of sarsen-like sandstone. Found principally as isolated blocks between Chesham and Ware (Figure 26), it has also been recorded as a continuous bed near St Albans, and similar conglomerates are known from sections of the Reading Beds in brickpits there. A local variant, containing large, subangular brown or grey flints, can be seen in the village of Bradenham, in Buckinghamshire.

The sarsens and analogous rocks are remnants of otherwise unconsolidated beds, that were patchily cemented by precipitation of silica just below the ground surface; the surrounding uncemented material has long since been washed away. Such 'silcretes' are characteristic of arid or semi-arid climates. They probably formed during early Neogene (Miocene) times, when an erosion surface was formed across a range of Palaeogene strata.

NEOGENE

At some time after deposition of the Barton Beds, there was a significant fall in sea level. Sedimentation continued in the North Sea during parts of the late Eocene and the succeeding Oligocene and Miocene epochs, but no marine sediments of this age are known within the London and Thames Valley region. However, to the south-east of the region, pebbly sands containing moulds of marine molluscs infill solution pipes in the Chalk on the North Downs of east Kent. These '**Lenham Beds**' are probably of late Miocene age, and are evidence of a marine transgression which may well have encroached into this region. Nevertheless, for periods of millions of years, the region was land, and pre-existing deposits were weathered and dissected. The cementation of the sarsens of the region may date from this time.

The eastern part of the London Basin and adjoining East Anglia was again covered by the sea in late Pliocene times, and shallow-marine deposition

Plate 17 Sarsen sandstones were once widespread on the chalk downlands. Fyfield Down National Nature Reserve, near Marlborough, Wiltshire, is one of the few places where they can still be seen in their natural state (A11411).

continued into the earliest part of the Pleistocene. During this interval, the sandy deposits of the **Red Crag** and **Norwich Crag**, were laid down (Table 8). The more complete crag succession in East Anglia provides evidence of oscillations in climate which foreshadowed the major Pleistocene glaciations of Britain.The crag deposits are preserved in parts of Essex, and extend into East Anglia as a more or less continuous sheet of sediment (Figure 26). They are generally very poorly exposed, being largely concealed beneath Pleistocene fluvial and glacial deposits. The deposits are generally less than 20 m in thickness, but their deeper-water equivalents in the North Sea Basin may be up to 600 m thick.

The base of the crag deposits lies at about 13 to 14 m above sea level (OD) at Walton-on-the-Naze. It climbs westward at approximately 1 m per kilometre, reaching about 90 m above OD near Elsenham. Beyond, there are scattered small outliers at least as far west as Rothamsted in Hertfordshire, where fragments of ferruginous, shelly sandstone were recovered at 130 m above OD. Possibly equivalent deposits occur very locally on the North Downs near Guildford, notably at Netley Heath, at about 180 m above OD. There, sands are patchily cemented into a ferruginous gritty sandstone, which has yielded molluscs including the typical Red Crag form *Corbulomya complanata* (J Sowerby). The present-day altitude of the crag deposits, and their consistent eastwards tilt, are best explained by post-depositional tectonic movements, indicating a considerable rise of the land concomitant with subsidence of the North Sea Basin during the Quaternary Period.

The crag deposits of Essex can be divided into two units. The lower of these is the Red Crag, variably ferruginous, medium- to coarse-grained and relatively poorly sorted sands, which are locally very shelly. At their base, they commonly contain large wave-rolled flints. Some fractured flints were once thought to be crude implements ('eoliths') fashioned by early man, but they are now known to be of natural origin. The unit contains phosphatic nodules and pebbles, mostly material reworked from the underlying London Clay.

Characteristic shelly sands of the Red Crag can be seen in the cliff sections of Walton-on-the-Naze, the most accessible and best-known exposure in the region. They show large-scale cross-bedding produced by the migration of large sand-waves (dunes) in a tidal sea. The most common fossils at Walton are bivalves including *Astarte obliquata* J Sowerby, *Cardium parkinsoni* J Sowerby, *Glycymeris glycymeris* (Linnaeus) and *Spisula arcuata* (J Sowerby), gastropods such as *Hinia granulata* (J Sowerby), *Natica multipunctata* S V Wood, *Neptunea contraria* (Linnaeus) and *Nucella tetragona* (J Sowerby), and the echinoderm *Echinocyamus pusillus* (Müller). The fossils are mostly broken up, having been transported over the sea floor by powerful tidal currents. The upper part of the deposit is largely decalcified, and zones of secondary limonite-cementation occur.

The Red Crag is succeeded by finer-grained, better sorted, unfossiliferous sands (the 'Chillesford Sand Member'), that can be traced into the Norwich Crag of south-east Suffolk. Ripple- and dune-bedding structures indicate bidirectional currents, implying deposition in a shallow, tidal sea. Soft-sediment deformation structures are locally abundant, indicating rapid sedimentation.

The foraminifera and molluscs in the crag deposits, indicate a temperate climate. Pollen derived from the adjacent land indicates that the vegetation was dominated by pine forest during the deposition of the Red Crag, and mixed oak forest during deposition of the Norwich Crag. There was probably a long break in sedimentation between the Red and Norwich Crags (Table 8), because additional deposits intervene in parts of East Anglia, some with indications of cold climate.

The Red and Norwich Crag deposits are regarded as of earliest Pleistocene age in many accounts. However, by international definition, the base of the Pleistocene is placed (by magnetostratigraphy) at 1.64 million years before present, somewhat younger than the traditional usage in Britain. According to this definition, the crag deposits of the region are of latest Pliocene age (Table 8). Palynological evidence from Walton-on-the-Naze suggests that the deposits there equate with strata on the continent which are about 2.4 million years old.

Marine deposition in the region was terminated by a glacio-eustatic marine regression, marked on the Suffolk coast by the Chillesford Clay and the Easton Bavents Clay, which yield fossils indicating pronounced climatic cooling. Following this cold episode, shallow-marine deposition returned to northern East Anglia, but there is no evidence of subsequent marine incursions within this region.

9 Quaternary

The Quaternary Period spans the last 1.64 million years (Ma). The main part comprises the Pleistocene Epoch, which ended 10 000 years ago (Table 9). During this interval, vast sheets of glacier ice advanced from polar regions to cover much of Britain, and so the Pleistocene is often termed the 'ice-age'. However, there were numerous climatic fluctuations, during the Pleistocene with cold or 'glacial' phases, alternating with more temperate 'interglacial' phases. During some of the interglacials, the climate was warmer than at the present time. The succeeding Holocene (or Recent) Epoch, which spans the last 10 000 years, should probably be regarded as an interglacial, with the implication that glaciers may return to the British Isles at some time in the future.

Unravelling British Quaternary history is difficult because of the complex and discontinuous nature of the sediments and the incompleteness of the stratigraphical record. The deposits of the glacial phases are particularly difficult to date directly, but river and lake sediments laid down during the interglacials may contain fossil plant and animal material which hold the key to Quaternary chronology. Studies of fossils from these sediments, particularly pollen, has made it possible to characterise individual interglacials and, by deducing the relative age of associated glacial deposits from stratigraphical principles, a chronostratigraphical framework has been built up.

Using these techniques, it seemed by the 1970s that there was good evidence for three glaciations, the Anglian, Wolstonian and Devensian stages, and three temperate interglacials, the Cromerian, Hoxnian and Ipswichian stages, in the later part of the Pleistocene. The Devensian glacial stage was followed by the Flandrian interglacial stage which corresponds with the Holocene Epoch (Table 9). The Anglian glaciation was the most extensive, with ice reaching north and east London, probably the only time that it has encroached into the region. Additionally, there seemed to be some scanty evidence for earlier Pleistocene glacial–interglacial cycles.

In contrast to the situation on land, the slow sedimentation in the deep oceans tends to be more or less continuous, and in some places it may chronicle the whole of the Quaternary. Since the 1950s, studies of oxygen-isotope variation in the shells of foraminifera from these sediments, have revealed the way in which global ice volume and temperature has fluctuated with time. Similar techniques applied more recently to ice cores from Antarctica and Greenland, and to travertine deposits from caves, have yielded comparable results. The resultant graph of temperature fluctuation during the Quaternary (Table 9) appears to show a regular periodicity, which may be caused by cyclical irregularities in the orbit of the earth around the sun (Milankovitch cycles). Most significantly, the graph shows a far greater number of cold–temperate cycles than are recognised in the 'traditional'

Table 9   Correlation of principal Quaternary deposits in the London and Thames Valley region.

SYSTEM/SERIES	BRITISH STAGE	Representative fluvial deposits UPPER THAMES	Representative fluvial deposits MIDDLE THAMES	Representative fluvial deposits LOWER THAMES/ESSEX	Oxygen Isotope Stage	AGE (ka)
HOLOCENE	FLANDRIAN	ALLUVIUM	ALLUVIUM	ALLUVIUM	1	
PLEISTOCENE — Upper	DEVENSIAN	NORTH-MOOR	BURIED CHANNEL	BURIED CHANNEL	2	
	DEVENSIAN		SHEPPERTON	SHEPPERTON	3	
					4	
	IPSWICHIAN		KEMPTON PARK	EAST TILBURY MARSHES	a / c / 5 / e	100
PLEISTOCENE — Middle	WOLSTONIAN (Interglacial 'Ilfordian' of some authors)	SUMMER-TOWN-RADLEY			6	
			TAPLOW	MUCKING	7	200
					8	
	(Interglacial ?type Hoxnian)	WOLVER-COTE	LYNCH HILL	CORBETS TEY	9	300
			? Glacial Deposits		10	
	ANGLIAN / HOXNIAN (Interglacial 'Swancombe' of some authors)	HAN-BOROUGH	BOYN HILL	ORSETT HEATH	11	400
			BLACK PARK			
			Glacial Deposits		12	
					13	500
					14	
	CROMERIAN COMPLEX	Northern Drift	High level gravels	Kesgrave Sands and Gravels	15	600
					16 to ?21	
PLEISTOCENE — Lower					?22	not to scale
					to	
					c63	1640

Deep-sea oxygen isotope variation (COLD ← → WARM)

scheme of glacial and interglacial stages for the British Quaternary, suggesting that the latter is greatly oversimplified.

To resolve controversies such as this, absolute age determinations are important. Of the methods used, radiocarbon is suitable only within the Holocene and the last part of the Devensian Stage, and is of little use beyond about 30 000 years before present (BP). For older materials, ages obtained by uranium series dating or thermoluminescence and electron spin resonance techniques are often subject to large errors or uncertainties. A promising method of relative dating utilises the time-dependent change in amino acids within the shells of molluscs such as the snails (terrestrial or aquatic) and bivalves that are commonly found in interglacial sediments and, more rarely, in fluvial sediments dating from the milder parts of glacials. A timescale based on this technique was published in 1989; this tied shell-bearing sediments to the temperate oxygen-isotope stages and related these to the standard glacial/interglacial cycles of the Middle and Upper Pleistocene. This timescale recognised four interglacials after the Anglian glaciation, whereas the pollen-based 'traditional' chronology had identified only two (Table 9).

Because of these recent developments, many aspects of the Pleistocene chronology of the London and Thames Valley region are still topics of continued research and debate, and the chronology shown in Table 9 is provisional.

The outcrop of Quaternary deposits occupies about a third of the region (Figure 1). They are predominantly of Pleistocene age, but are variable both in lithology and in the environment of deposition. The most important deposits for unravelling the geological history of the region are those laid down by rivers. The greater part of the region lies within the catchment of the Thames. A number of rivers in Essex, which now flow into the North Sea, may be regarded as part of the Thames system, because they join the drowned extension of its valley offshore. Small parts of the catchments of the River Ouse and Bristol Avon are represented in the north and west of the region respectively.

PLEISTOCENE

Pleistocene deposits related to the River Thames are widespread in the region (Figure 29) and occur typically as terraces on the valley sides (Figure 30). These terraces represent ancient floodplain deposits that became isolated as the river cut downwards to lower levels; the highest terrace deposits are therefore the oldest. River terrace deposits are composed primarily of gravel and sand, rarely more than a few metres thick. Composition varies greatly, depending on the source material available in the river's catchment. Generally, soft materials such as chalk and clay were removed during transport by the river, leaving only the more durable rocks, notably flint and limestone. For this reason, river gravels form important sources of

Figure 29   Distribution of principal Quaternary fluvial and glacial deposits (greatly simplified), and localities mentioned in the text. Note that Holocene river alluvium is not separately distinguished from other post-Anglian fluvial deposits except in Lower Thames and coastal area. Other Quaternary deposits, such as clay-with-flints and slope deposits, though extensive in parts of the region, are not shown.

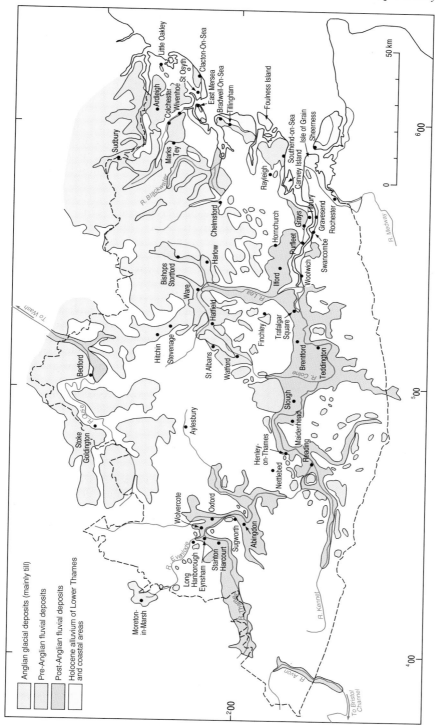

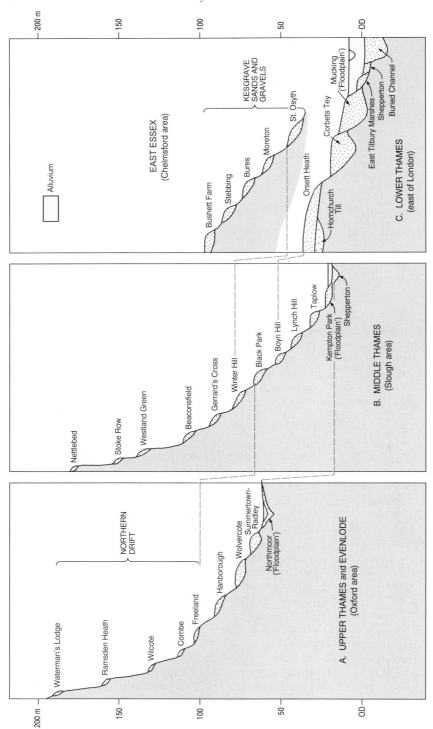

Figure 30   Diagram illustrating the height relationships, nomenclature and correlation of the terrace deposits of the River Thames. See also Table 9.

aggregate for commerce. Locally, the gravels may be overlain by superficial cover of silty loam, often described as 'brickearth'. In some cases, this may represent the original overbank mud of the river, laid down during floods.

The reasons for terrace formation are not fully understood, but it is generally agreed that the process is related to the climatic cycles of the Quaternary. The main periods of gravel deposition and the intervening phases of downcutting are attributed to glacial episodes, when erosion was more intense, and when rivers were swollen during the spring melt. Sediment supply and deposition was more restricted during interglacials, and so warm-climate sediments are generally rare within terrace sequences. However, fossiliferous interglacial deposits of silt and clay are found locally in channels, both beneath and within cold-climate gravels.

Pre-Anglian deposits of the River Thames

The basic pattern of Thames drainage was established during the Palaeogene and Neogene periods, when earth movements caused gradual uplift of western Britain and the creation of the broad Weald Anticline and London Basin syncline. By the beginning of the Pleistocene, an ancestor of the river Thames formed the main route of drainage from the London Basin into the North Sea. The main headwaters of this river would have corresponded with the present Kennet catchment. The modern Upper Thames (above the Goring Gap) may have been just one of several tributaries flowing down the Chalk dip slope which, at that time, extended farther north-west than its present limits. Similar tributaries, most notably an ancestor of the River Medway, entered the Thames from the south (Figure 31).

At times, the early Thames valley would have been drowned at its downstream end by encroachment of the sea. High-level planation surfaces in north London and the Chilterns were formerly regarded as evidence of a more widespread Pliocene or early Pleistocene marine transgression. Associated deposits composed predominantly of rounded flint pebbles occur at many sites, up to, and above, 200 m above OD. These 'Pebble Gravels' were once thought to be beach deposits, but most are now regarded as early Pleistocene deposits of Thames tributaries, the pebbles having been reworked from Palaeogene formations. However, two small outcrops, at Little Heath, near Berkhampstead (about 165 m above OD), and at Lane End near High Wycombe (about 198 m above OD), may indeed be of marine origin, but the evidence is inconclusive.

At Nettlebed, high on the Chilterns, a small outcrop of flint-rich gravel is thought to be the oldest surviving deposit of the River Thames. The gravel lies some 170 m higher than the present course of the river, and is several kilometres distant, giving an indication of the vast amount of erosion that has taken place during the Quaternary. Associated with this gravel, a remnant of interglacial sediments may be the oldest in Britain outside East Anglia.

To the south and south-east, at lower levels, a whole suite of gravel terraces can be traced on the north slopes of the Thames valley between Reading and Maidenhead (Figure 30). These terraces represent successive levels of the river which, during each phase of downcutting, migrated farther to the south. The high-level terraces are relatively poorly preserved and remote from the modern course of the river. They were not originally recognised as products of the Thames and, because they contain a significant proportion of 'erratic'

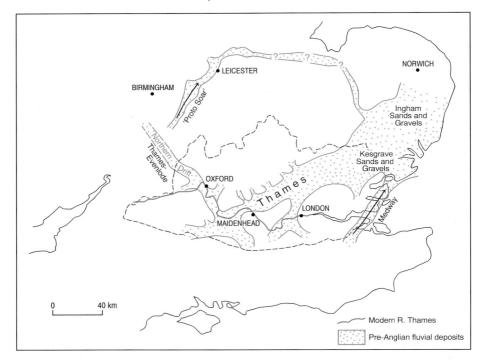

Figure 31 Reconstruction of the pre-Anglian drainage system, showing the probable original extent of pre-Anglian fluvial deposits. Compare Figure 29. Note that the present Thames downstream of Maidenhead, did not exist until after the Anglian glaciation.

material from beyond the present catchment, some were classified as 'Glacial Sand and Gravel'.

Similar deposits also cap high ground in the Oxford–Abingdon area, and on the Cotswolds to the north-west, particularly in and around the valley of the River Evenlode, a tributary that meets the Thames at Eynsham (Figure 30). They comprise clayey gravels and pebbly clays containing pebbles of quartzite, quartz and various other exotic rocks. These deposits have been termed Northern Drift because the occurrence of these exotic stones, most of which can be matched with lithologies from the Triassic 'Bunter Pebble Beds' (now Kidderminster Formation) of the Midlands. Small quantities of volcanic rocks, probably from north Wales, also occur. Because of its content of far-travelled pebbles, the Northern Drift had been thought to be a glacial deposit, but it is now considered to represent a degraded suite of river terrace deposits, equivalent to those forming the high-level terraces downstream (Figure 30). These terrace deposits indicate the existence of an Early Pleistocene Evenlode–Thames river that drained a far larger area than the modern Thames catchment, including much of the Midlands and possibly parts of north and central Wales (Figure 31).

Beyond the Maidenhead area, where the present River Thames turns towards the south-east, the high-level, quartzite-rich terrace gravels of the early

Thames can be traced north-eastwards towards Watford, where they pass beneath the deposits of the later Anglian glaciation (Figure 29). Similar quartzite-bearing gravels occur in Essex and East Anglia. Known as the Kesgrave Sands and Gravels, these are now recognised as the downstream correlatives of the early Thames deposits, indicating that the pre-Anglian route of the river lay well to the north of London, passing through the Vale of St Albans (Figure 3) and thence into southern East Anglia (Figure 31). The Kesgrave Sands and Gravels have been subdivided into a number of terraces corresponding with the high-level terraces upstream of Maidenhead (Figure 30). These terraces are particularly well preserved between Colchester and the Essex coast (Figure 29); studies of the gravels there show that the River Medway was then an important southern tributary of the Thames, joining it near Clacton-on-Sea. The Medway gravels, characterised by the presence of rocks of southerly derivation, particularly chert from the Lower Greensand of the Weald, form a sequence of degraded high-level terraces that can be traced across eastern Essex, from the Rayleigh Hills to Bradwell-on-Sea (Figure 31).

Studies of the pebble composition of each of the high-level terrace gravels suggests that the exotic material entered the Thames system in a series of pulses, possibly resulting from repeated glaciations in the uplands of north Wales. The exotic material is present in greatest quantities in the Gerrards Cross Gravel and its equivalents (Figure 30). It is progressively diminished in the younger terraces, although still present as a result of reworking from older deposits. Thus the direct supply of exotic rocks was cut off after the deposition of the Gerrards Cross Gravel, perhaps 750 000 years ago, when the catchment of the Thames appears to have contracted to approximately its present extent. This may have been caused by capture of the Thames headwaters by the 'Proto-Soar River', north of the Cotswolds. Unlike the modern south-westward-flowing Avon of that area, the Proto-Soar flowed north-eastwards (Figure 31), probably veering eastwards near Leicester, and thence to the North Sea through East Anglia. There, the deposits of this river, the Ingham Sands and Gravels, interdigitate with the Kesgrave Sands and Gravels.

The record of pre-Anglian terraces, which are younger than the Gerrards Cross Gravel, is fragmentary. One important deposit thought to be from this interval occurs at Sugworth, near Abingdon, where silts infill a channel, buried beneath later gravels. The deposit yields molluscs, mammals, insects and pollen, and probably dates from the early Mid Pleistocene 'Cromerian Complex' which, although formerly thought to be a single interglacial, is now known to include at least four interglacials, separated by cold episodes. Comparable 'Cromerian' sediments are known within the Kesgrave Sands and Gravels; probably three different interglacials are represented at Ardleigh, Little Oakley and Wivenhoe, to the north and east of Colchester (Figure 29). The Little Oakley deposits are particularly important, containing abundant remains of mammals, molluscs, ostracods and small vertebrates, as well as pollen.

By the beginning of the Anglian Stage, the River Thames had already established its most southerly course up to that time. This course, represented by the Winter Hill Gravel and its downstream equivalents, has been traced through the Vale of St Albans where, as the Westmill Lower Gravel, it is well preserved beneath Anglian glacial deposits. Eastwards, the buried gravels continue beneath Harlow and Chelmsford, and there turn northwards towards Colchester. From Colchester, the gravels extend eastwards to

Clacton-on-Sea (Figure 32). There, they are known as the St Osyth Gravel, and form the youngest terrace of the Kesgrave Sands and Gravels (Figure 30).

Anglian glaciation and the diversion of the Thames

Despite the numerous glacial episodes of the Quaternary, a major ice sheet probably occupied this region only during the Anglian Stage. This is generally equated with Oxygen Isotope Stage 12, which began about 470 000 years ago (Table 9). At this time, ice advanced southward into the region, eroding the ground over which it passed. This material was deposited at the base of the ice as it moved, or was dumped when it eventually melted away, to form a sheet of till (boulder clay). Within the region, the till contains numerous fragments of chalk and flint, together with smaller proportions of other rocks, including rare lithologies from as far afield as Scandinavia. This rock debris may range in size from silt grains to boulders, and locally 'rafts' of bedrock many metres across may occur. The matrix consists of bluish grey clay composed largely of ground-up Jurassic and Lower Cretaceous mudstone, with derived fossils including *Gryphaea* and belemnites.

Closely associated with the till are lenses and sheets of gravel deposited by meltwater streams, that ran beneath the ice, and issued from the ice front. They contain similar rocks to those found in the till, including relatively soft ones such as chalk. In places, subglacial drainage under considerable pressure cut channels into the bedrock, modifying existing valleys of the buried landscape. Many examples of such channels, buried by glacial deposits, have been proved by boreholes in the region, for example at Hitchin, Bishops Stortford and Sudbury in Hertfordshire. A dissected sheet of till and associated deposits occurs over a wide area in the north, and north-east of the region (Figure 29); outliers are found around Moreton-in-Marsh. The deposits vary greatly in thickness, and may exceed 100m where they infill buried valleys in the bedrock surface. Their distribution gives an indication of the maximum extent of the ice sheet (Figure 32), which was restricted to the northern part of the region, never encroaching south of the present River Thames.

At sites in the Chelmsford area and in the Vale of St Albans, Anglian glacial deposits overlie the gravels of the early River Thames. In the Vale of St Albans, ice invaded from the north-east, blocking the original route of Thames drainage, and depositing the Ware Till. At this time, ice encroached upstream as far as the Harlow area, forming a lake in the area around Ware. As the ice continued to advance along the vale, a second lake formed around Watford. The silts and clays laid down in these lakes are laminated; these laminae may represent annual 'varves' caused by the seasonal cycle of freeze and thaw, and indicate that the lakes existed for several hundred years.

The damming of the original Thames valley by ice forced the drainage southwards, and the River Thames took up a course approximating to its modern route flowing through London, towards Southend-on-Sea (Figure 32). There, the Thames joined the Medway to flow across eastern Essex, rejoining its original course near Clacton-on-Sea.

Deposits in the Vale of St Albans record three further Anglian ice advances, as well as the initiation of the River Lea and the Colne as outwash streams carrying meltwater from the ice fronts into the diverted Thames (Figure 32). The most extensive of these later advances was responsible for

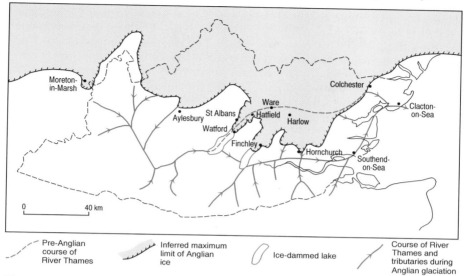

Figure 32 The extent of Anglian glaciation in the region, the blockage of the Vale of St Albans by Anglian ice, and the diversion of the River Thames.

the glacial sediments found around Finchley, and also those at Hornchurch, where they are overlain by terrace gravels of the diverted Thames.

As the climate became milder at the end of the Anglian glaciation, the ice gradually melted and large volumes of meltwater, carrying gravelly detritus, flowed down the Thames. The Black Park Terrace dates from this time; it includes outwash material from ice which occupied the Vale of St Albans. However, it has been suggested that outwash from Moreton-in-Marsh, Aylesbury, and north Buckinghamshire may grade into the much younger Wolvercote Terrace of the Oxford area (Figure 30). If this is so, it would indicate that the Anglian glaciation consisted of two major phases (probably Oxygen Isotope Stages 12 and 10), separated by an interglacial (Table 9).

As blocks of ice buried within the till melted, small lakes formed in 'kettle holes' on the surface. These lakes were slowly infilled with silt or peat, particularly during the subsequent interglacial period. An example occurs at Hatfield, and another was recently exposed during road construction near Stevenage. More extensive interglacial lake deposits occur at Marks Tey near Colchester, and have provided an important pollen record of the Hoxnian interglacial.

Post-Anglian, Pre-Devensian deposits of the Thames

In the period between the Anglian glaciation and the Devensian Stage, the Thames and its tributaries became established in their modern-day valleys. The terrace deposits, laid down during this time are generally well preserved.

Three terraces are recognised downstream from London, with additional gravels buried by the alluvium of the modern floodplain (Figure 30). The highest and oldest terrace, equated with the Boyn Hill Terrace of the Slough area, is formed by the Orsett Heath Gravel. Its deposits contain interglacial sediments at Swanscombe (Plate 22), which is of international renown for the discovery there of the 'Swanscombe Skull' and associated flint artefacts. The locality is also well known as the source of Pleistocene mammal bones and mollusc shells. Although there remain some uncertainties because of the lack of pollen data, the Swanscombe sediments are attributed to the first inter- glacial after the Anglian diversion of the Thames. Although this has generally been equated with the British Hoxnian Stage, doubts about the true age of the Hoxnian type-site, in Suffolk, to the north of the region, have led to the use of the term 'Swanscombe interglacial'; this episode is thought to correlate with Oxygen Isotope Stage 11 (Table 9).

The subsequent terrace in the Lower Thames sequence is formed by the Corbets Tey Gravel. It was originally mapped as the 'Taplow Terrace', but is now believed to equate with the Lynch Hill Terrace of the area upstream of London (Figure 30). The deposits incorporate interglacial sediments at a number of sites, notably Ilford (High Road), Purfleet and also Grays, where a brickpit yielded a rich fauna of small vertebrates in the early years of the twentieth century. The sediments at Purfleet (and probably also at Grays) include laminated beds of estuarine origin, recording an episode of high sea level. The fossil plant and animal remains from these localities are not diag- nostic of any particular interglacial, but their position in the terrace sequence suggests deposition in the second of the four post-Anglian interglacials, that correlated with Oxygen Isotope Stage 9 (Table 9), perhaps the same age as the Hoxnian type-site.

The lowest terrace above the floodplain of the Thames is traditionally known as the 'Floodplain Terrace', but terraces of different ages are repre- sented at different points along the river. East of London, the Floodplain Terrace, formed by the Mucking Gravel, is equated with the Taplow Terrace upstream (Figure 30). Interglacial deposits are known in several places, notably at Ilford (Uphall Pit) and Aveley, again with evidence for estuarine conditions during part of the interglacial. These sites have yielded skeletons of woolly mammoth, straight-tusked elephant, extinct rhinoceros, lion, bear, giant deer, horse and many other animals. The deposits have generally been attributed to the last (Ipswichian) interglacial on the basis of pollen analysis, but this view has been challenged by palaeontologists working on mammals and molluscs. Recently, amino acid analyses of shells from such sites have also indicated that an earlier episode is represented, and it is now assigned to the third of the four post-Anglian interglacials, namely Oxygen Isotope Stage 7, which has been termed the 'Ilfordian' by some workers (Table 9).

The last interglacial, the Ipswichian, is not known in terrace sediments down- stream from London; any deposits of this age lie beneath the modern flood- plain (Figure 30). However, Ipswichian deposits are known within the Kempton Park Gravel (forming the 'Upper Floodplain Terrace') at Brentford and also at Trafalgar Square in central London, where they were discovered during building excavations. They contain abundant remains of mammals, including hippopotamus, which (as the modern species *H. amphibius*) is thought to have lived in Britain only during Ipswichian times. The Ipswichian interglacial is cor- related with the oldest part (5e) of Oxygen Isotope Stage 5 (Table 9).

Although the Lower Thames provides the most complete record of post- Anglian Pleistocene deposits in Britain, important elements of this story are also recorded in other parts of the region. The last three interglacials are probably represented by channel deposits associated with terrace gravels near Oxford, for example at Wolvercote (? Oxygen Isotope Stage 9), Stanton Harcourt (Stage 7), and Eynsham (Ipswichian, Stage 5e). The older Swanscombe interglacial (Stage 11) may be represented by reworked mammal bones within the gravels of the Hanborough Terrace at Long Hanborough (Figure 30; Plate 18). The terraces of the Thames–Medway route across eastern Essex include correlatives of the Orsett Heath and Corbets Tey gravels, and younger Pleistocene terraces are represented offshore, illustrating the gradual eastward migration of the river in this area. Channel sediments of Swancombe interglacial age are known at several sites, notably in the cliffs and foreshore at Clacton-on-Sea, where they have yielded abundant animal and plant fossils, as well as evidence of the important 'Clactonian' flint industry. Another Swanscombe interglacial site occurs at East Mersea (Figure 29). Just to the west, deposits of the River Blackwater contain sediments dating from the Ipswichian interglacial; this is also represented by deposits of the River Chelmer at Chelmsford.

Of the other rivers within the region, the Ouse, which flows through Bedford to the Wash, provides an important sedimentary record. At Biddenham, immediately west of Bedford, terrace deposits contain inter-

Plate 18 Gravels of the Hanborough Terrace of the River Evenlode, at Long Hanborough, Oxfordshire (1975). The gravel is predominantly composed of Middle Jurassic limestone pebbles. The 'pipes' infilled with darker loam are due to localised solution of these clasts; they are analogous to the solution pipes commonly found in the Chalk (A11951).

glacial molluscs, mammal bones and flint artefacts; these probably date from Oxygen Isotope Stage 9. Farther west at Stoke Goldington, deposits containing molluscs, insects and plant remains, are attributed to the Stage 7 interglacial. Sites on a lower terrace near Bedford, have yielded Ipswichian faunas with hippopotamus remains.

Devensian deposits in the Thames Valley

The traditional chronostratigraphical scheme for the Late Pleistocene of Britain recognises a single Devensian glacial stage after the Ipswichian interglacial. The Devensian Stage incorporates at least three short episodes of milder climate known as 'interstadials'. The first two, known respectively as the Chelford and Upton Warren interstadials, occurred before the main Devensian glaciation. They were thought to have occurred in the middle part of the Devensian Stage (Oxygen Isotope Stage 3), but some workers now consider them to represent parts (a and c) of temperate Oxygen Isotope Stage 5, of which the Ipswichian Interglacial is only the earliest, and warmest, part (5e; Table 9). This view is supported by the presence of sediments of both these interstadials, within the Kempton Park Gravel, which also includes Ipswichian deposits (at Brentford and Trafalgar Square). Sediments of the Upton Warren Interstadial occur at Marlow, Isleworth and Kempton Park, and those of the Chelford Interstadial are known from tributary valleys, on the River Wey near Farnham.

The main part of the Devensian Stage (Oxygen Isotope stages 4–2), corresponds to the period between about 70 000 and 13 000 years BP. It is thought to be represented by cold-climate gravel deposits that form the upper part of the Kempton Park Gravel (above the interglacial and interstadial sediments) and the younger Shepperton Gravel. The latter forms the 'Lower Floodplain Terrace', which underlies alluvium in the London area. The coldest part of the Devensian, the Dimlington Stadial, occurred between about 25 000 and 13 000 years BP. At that time, ice-sheets covered Scotland, Wales and northern England as far south as north Norfolk, but the London and Thames Valley region lay in the 'periglacial' zone, beyond the ice. Because of the enormous volume of water locked up in the expanded polar ice-caps, sea level was as much as 120 m lower than at present. The North Sea was much reduced or absent, Britain was joined to the European mainland, and the Thames extended far to the east of the present coast. Downcutting in the Lower Thames created a deep channel that has been traced offshore by seismic methods. This channel was subsequently infilled with gravel as sea level rose again towards the end of the Devensian. These deposits, equivalent to younger parts of the Shepperton Gravels, now form the 'Buried Channel' beneath Holocene alluvium (Figure 30).

Dateable deposits from the Dimlington Stadial are generally rare, but there are notable occurrences beneath the gravels underlying the floodplain of the River Lea. At Ponders End, Broxbourne and Stratford, broken rafts of a peaty 'arctic plant bed' contain remains of mosses and dwarf forms of birch and willow that indicate a severely cold climate.

The final part of the Devensian Stage, or 'Late-glacial' interval, began with the Windermere Interstadial. This is well represented by peats in upland areas of the British Isles and has been dated by radiocarbon methods to between about 13 000 and 11 000 years BP. The brief Loch Lomond Stadial followed, during which cold conditions returned and glaciers formed once more in the Scottish Highlands. The climate finally ameliorated at the beginning of the Holocene, about 10 000 years BP. Late-glacial deposits occur commonly beneath the floodplains of the Thames and its tributaries, but are rarely seen in open section, since any gravel pits quickly fill with water. However, they have been documented at Northmoor and Farmoor near Oxford, at Abingdon, and at West Drayton and Colnbrook, in the valley of the Colne.

Other Pleistocene deposits

'Clay-with-flints' is a descriptive name applied to a range of deposits that cap the high chalk downland of the region. It is particularly widespread on the Chilterns, but is also present in the Berkshire, Marlborough and North Downs. Typically, the deposits comprise reddish brown clay or sandy clay, containing abundant flint pebbles, including unrolled nodules with their white cortex intact. Other pebble lithologies, such as sarsen sandstone, occur sporadically. The lower surface of the deposit is typically highly irregular, and Clay-with-Flints commonly infills deep solution pipes and fissures in the underlying Chalk. The bulk of the material seems to be the insoluble residue left after dissolution of the Chalk by weathering, with an added contribution from Palaeogene sediments of which there may be no other remaining evidence. The development of Clay-with-flints probably began in Neogene times, and may have continued throughout much of the Pleistocene.

Loess comprises wind-blown silt which was deposited during cold, dry episodes of the Quaternary. It is particularly characteristic of areas surrounding glaciated districts, where abundant fine-grained material was available from tills and outwash deposits, and where there was little vegetation to prevent the wind picking up this material. Thick loess is found over much of Europe and Asia. It is typically an unbedded, uniform deposit, characterised by vertical prismatic jointing; it is generally calcareous and may contain small concretions. In Britain, deposits of loess occur in east Kent and in the Southend area, and a proportion of loess may be present in soils, slope deposits, and in some of the 'brickearths' that overlie many river terraces. Most of these deposits are probably of late Devensian age. Older loess has contributed to slope deposits in the Northfleet area of Kent, and is preserved in pockets beneath the Anglian till in north-eastern Essex.

Slope deposits form an important part of the Pleistocene record; they include the 'head' of geological maps. They formed principally beyond the ice limits during the glacial phases of the Pleistocene, when erosion was accelerated because of the arctic climate and lack of vegetation. Debris of frost-weathered material, which accumulated during the winters, formed a slurry when the snows melted in the spring. This gradually flowed down slopes, to form a poorly bedded deposit of very variable character which may resemble till. Where chalk is the principal component, the sediments have been termed 'coombe deposits', or 'coombe rock' where they are cemented. Coombe deposits are widespread in the dry valleys of the Downs and Chilterns and are also found interbedded with some of the river terrace deposits in the Lower Thames valley. In many areas, slope deposits built up during successive cold episodes. The history of such sequences may be difficult to unravel, unless fossiliferous interglacial deposits occur in the succession, as at Pitstone, near Tring. There, deposits of both Oxygen Isotope Stage 7 and the Ipswichian interglacial have been found within chalky and sandy slope deposits. Buried soils may also separate slope deposits of different ages. Interglacial soils are rare in Britain, but a well-documented example, probably of Stage 7 age, occurs at Baker's Hole, Northfleet, within a sequence dominated by slope deposits. It is associated with sediments containing abundant mammal remains and Palaeolithic artefacts. Soils are more common within the widespread slope deposits that date from the latter part of the Devensian Stage. Soils in such deposits occur at Halling and Holborough near Rochester in Kent, where snail faunas and radiocarbon dating suggest the Windermere Interstadial. At Pitstone, a double soil also dates from this period.

Periglacial structures affect the upper parts of many Pleistocene deposits, both drift and bedrock. They indicate the development of permafrost during the colder parts of the Pleistocene, having formed mainly in the near-surface, 'active zone' which was subjected to a seasonal cycle of freeze and thaw. Similar structures are still forming today, in areas marginal to the ice-bound polar regions of the world. Many types of periglacial structures are recognised: sections in gravel pits may show vertically orientated pebbles and contorted bedding (involutions or festoons) resulting from frost-heave, ice-wedge casts (in which later deposits infill wide fissures opened up by the growth of ground-ice; Plate 19), and sand wedges filling thermal contraction cracks. On a larger scale, crop marks seen on aerial photographs sometimes show a polygonal pattern representing the plan view of networks of ice-wedge casts. Cambering (the movement and collapse of bedrock strata on slopes, valley bulging (the deformation of strata at the foot of slopes) and landslipping were also exacerbated by periglacial climatic regimes. These periglacial structures date mostly from the Devensian glaciation, but in rare cases, those formed during earlier periglacial episodes may be preserved beneath later Quaternary sediments. An example is the network of involutions and sand wedges in the top of the pre-Anglian Kesgrave Sands and Gravels, sometimes seen when the overlying glacial sediments are removed during quarrying.

The dry valleys that are such a characteristic feature of the Chilterns and North Downs, and of the limestone uplands of the Cotswolds, may also be a relic of a periglacial regime. Though found in areas of permeable bedrock which does not generally support a surface drainage system, the valleys were probably initiated by streams and rivers during periods when deep permafrost rendered the ground impermeable.

Deposits of **calcareous tufa** are quite common in the Cotswolds, along the Chilterns scarp and in some other places, where water saturated with calcium carbonate issues at springs. Most of these deposits are of Holocene age, and many continue to form at the present day. Older tufas are rare, but Middle Pleistocene deposits are found at Hitchin. They contain a snail fauna including species that today are found mostly in southern Europe, and a form whose closest modern equivalent occurs only in the Canary Islands. It may date from the Swanscombe Interglacial (Oxygen Isotope Stage 11).

Plate 19 Ice-wedge cast, near Colchester, Essex. Such structures indicate the development of permafrost during the cold phases of the Quaternary Period. This example affects the fluvial Kesgrave Sands and Gravels in the lower part of the face, but appears to be truncated by the overlying, paler glaciofluvial outwash gravels in the upper part. Such relationships give an indication of the age of the structures; in this case, the ice-wedge cast probably formed during the early part of the Anglian Stage, before glacier ice reached the area (A12508).

HOLOCENE

The Holocene epoch of the last 10 000 years corresponds with the Flandrian Stage of British Quaternary chronostratigraphy. Inland, it is represented principally by **alluvium**, forming the floodplains of the Thames and other rivers of the region. Alluvium is composed mainly of silt and clay, with seams of sand and gravel recording exceptional flood events. Lenses and beds of peat also occur locally, and are particularly well developed in the Lower Thames Valley. Alluvium commonly contains fossils such as molluscs, ostracods, insect remains, mammal bones and teeth, as well as common wood and other plant material including pollen, although relatively few pollen analyses have been published.

Early Holocene alluvium may contain Mesolithic artefacts, and a wealth of archaeological material has been recovered from many sites. Later in the Holocene, the clearance of woodland and cultivation of upland areas by Neolithic and later farmers, led to increased soil erosion, with the formation of loamy hillwash deposits on lower slopes and in valley bottoms, and to greatly increased alluvial sedimentation in the rivers. As dated by the contained artefacts and fossils, the most rapid rates of deposition of hillwash and alluvium occurred during the late Iron Age and in the Roman period. These processes continue to the present day, accelerated by modern intensive agriculture.

Towards the mouth of the Thames and other rivers, the Holocene alluvium, with its interbedded peats, interdigitates with, and grades into estuarine and coastal clays, silts and sands. This material, termed marine alluvium on some geological maps, flanks the Thames estuary and continues as a coastal plain along the Essex coast (Figure 29). Within the estuary, the width of the alluvium increases abruptly just east of Tilbury and Gravesend, where the bedrock changes from more resistant Chalk to more readily eroded Palaeogene beds. This widening of the Thames valley had a significant effect on Holocene sedimentation. Peat is more abundant upstream from this point, and downstream the alluvial deposits become increasingly marine in character, with less peat and more sand. The Holocene succession thickens towards the east, reaching almost 30m at Canvey Island and 36m at Foulness Island.

Sea level rose rapidly as the ice-caps began to melt towards the end of the Devensian, but was still very low (perhaps 65 m below OD) at the beginning of the Holocene. The shoreline lay far beyond its present position and the rivers of the region flowed eastward across a landscape that now lies beneath the North Sea. A complex system of these former river valleys, more or less infilled with sediment, has been found by offshore seismic surveys. With rising sea level, an extensive area of salt marsh and tidal flat had developed by approximately 8900 years BP, in the area of the present Thames estuary. Deposits of organic silt, clay and peat were formed in and around the channels; these deposits became progressively more estuarine in character as the transgression proceeded.

Sea level continued to rise throughout most of the Holocene, resulting in the accumulation of alluvial mud. However, beds of **peat** within the succession are thought to indicate temporary, minor falls in sea level, when plants colonised the exposed mudflats. In the Lower Thames, they record at least five cycles of transgression and regression (Figure 33) and a similar sequence has been recognised on the Essex coast. In the east, *Phragmites* reed and saltmarsh peats predominate, but with increasing freshwater influence upstream, oak and alder fen peats are found. Upstream of Tilbury, individual peats also show analogous vertical changes reflecting the changing sea level. The eastward dip of the peat beds suggests that a small component of the Holocene sea-level rise in the Thames Estuary results from eastward tilting of southern Britain during this time.

The basal peat at Tilbury is dated by radiocarbon to about 8300 years BP. At this time, the area now submerged beneath the Thames estuary was covered by woodland of oak and hazel. On the drier valley sides and uplands, pines, elms and oaks flourished, and close to the river channels, there was a reed-swamp or sedge-fen. Subsequently, sea level rose very rapidly (at about 13mm/annum), overwhelming the low-lying vegetated areas. The tidal head of the estuary probably reached Tilbury by around 7700 years BP. A regression at around 7000 years BP is recorded by a second bed of peat, which became submerged at 6600 years BP during the next transgression. The following regressive episode, commencing at about 6000

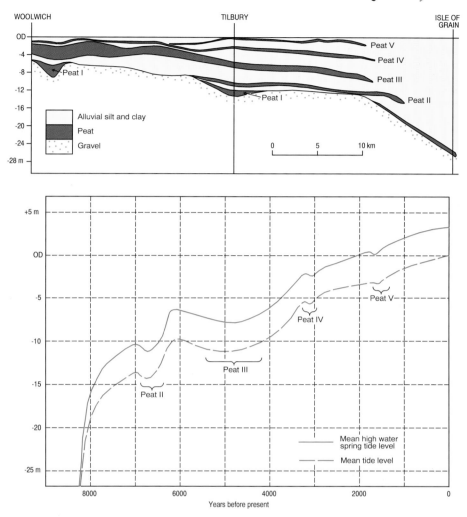

Figure 33 Diagrammatic cross-section illustrating the Holocene succession of the Lower Thames, and its relationship to inferred sea-level changes (after Devoy, 1977, 1979).

years BP, is marked by the thickest peat in the succession. At Northfleet, early Neolithic pottery has been found at Northfleet, in deposits dating from this time. Human influence was probably restricted to the occasional clearance of fen woodland and there is little evidence of prolonged habitation of the wetland areas. Transgression brought a return to brackish marine conditions in the inner estuary shortly after 4000 years BP. This event is marked by channels, infilled with intertidal sediments, that cut into the peat. The uppermost peat in the alluvial succession marks a regression during the 3rd and 4th centuries AD. Many coastal forts constructed by the Romans at this time were destroyed by the subsequent transgression, but that at Othona, near Bradwell-on-Sea, is still partly intact. This transgression still continues; sea level is currently rising at about 2 to 3 mm per year in the Thames estuary.

Today, the sediment load carried by the Thames is estimated to be about 200 000 tonnes per annum. The deposition of this material in the estuary is dependant, to a large degree, on tidal processes as a result of the mixing of fresh and saline water, which causes flocculation of clays, and the landward transport of sediment twice daily on the rising tide. Because of these factors, deposition occurs mainly between Woolwich and Gravesend. The mean spring tidal range at Sheerness is 5.1m, but this increases to 6.6 m at London Bridge, due to the funnelling effect within the estuary, which is further magnified by reclamation and embanking of former tidal flats. Upstream from London Bridge, the tidal range decreases towards Teddington, the limit of tidal influence.

Offshore, the current-swept environment permits very little mud to be deposited, but it is transported landward to accumulate on intertidal mudflats, such as those of east Essex, between Foulness Island and Bradwell-on-Sea (Figure 29). Between the saltmarshes and the upper tidal flats along this coast, large 'chenier' ridges occur (Plate 20). These ridges, up to 3 m high and 25 m wide, are composed almost entirely of shell debris. They result

Plate 20   Chenier ridge at Sales Point, near Bradwell-on-Sea, Essex. Such ridges are composed almost entirely of shells (in this case, mainly the cockle *Cerastoderma*; see inset) exhumed from the mudflats seawards of the ridge during storms (*Photographs P S Balson*) (GS2).

from the erosion of tidal-flat deposits, particularly at the margins of channels. Waves winnow away the fine sediment to expose the shells, which are cast up onto the marshes during storms. The ridges have been observed to move landward at rates of around 8 m per year. Older shell ridges, which have been found inland in the reclaimed marsh behind seawalls, represent relict shore-lines. The shells are mostly those of the common cockle *Cerastoderma edule* Linnaeus but, in the youngest deposits, the presence or otherwise of *Mya arenaria* Linnaeus (introduced into British waters in about 1600 AD) and the slipper limpet *Crepidula fornicata* Linnaeus (introduced in about 1880) gives an indication of relative age. Near Clacton-on-Sea, westward longshore drift has formed a series of sand spits. These have shown rapid rates of prolonga-tion; at Colne Point, Lee Spit has extended more than a kilometre since 1950.

Farther from the coast, modern sediments occur mostly in the form of elongate sandbanks that radiate away from the estuary mouth. Much of this sediment is reworked from Pleistocene fluvial sands or is derived from the coast of Essex and Suffolk to the north. Some of the banks are exposed at low water; they are generally covered with sandwaves (dunes), formed by strong tidal currents. The sandbanks are separated by narrow scoured channels, floored by gravels, generally only a few centimetres thick.

MAN IN THE QUATERNARY: THE STONE AGE

Fossil evidence from Africa shows that the earliest humans were in existence well before the beginning of the Pleistocene Period, but there is no indica-tion of the presence of man in the London and Thames Valley region before the Mid Pleistocene. However, during the milder interludes after the Anglian glaciation, the region seems to have been particularly favoured, and flint implements made by the inhabitants are known from many sites. Surprisingly, no artefacts are known from any of the sites attributed to the warm Ipswichian interglacial. It is thought that the climate during the preceding cold phase (Oxygen Isotope Stage 6) was so severe, that humans migrated far to the south. When sea level rose early in Ipswichian times, Britain was cut off from the European mainland, and man did not return until the sea level fell again, during the succeeding Devensian cold phase.

From the latter part of the nineteenth century onwards, it was apparent to archaeologists that the flint implements and weapons were contemporary with the remains of many extinct animals, and represented a long period of time prior to the appearance of modern man. Gradually, distinctive assem-blages of tool types (termed 'industries') began to be identified. To some extent, these coincide with the cultural evolution of man (Table 10). Some of the more important sites at which artefacts have been discovered are indicated in Figure 34.

Early Palaeolithic industries

Palaeolithic (Old Stone Age) flint artefacts are found in the greatest numbers in river terrace gravels, particularly along the main Thames valley and along the major tributaries, reflecting occupation along the banks of the river. In

Table 10   Stone Age industries: characteristic equipment, representative sites in the region and chronology.

	Period or Industry	Typical equipment	Important Thames Valley sites	Chronology
	NEOLITHIC	Polished axes Arrowheads Scrapers Sickles Pottery vessels	Staines causewayed enclosure	Holocene (c.5500 to 4000 BP)
	MESOLITHIC	Blades Microliths Hafted axes Bone and antler tools/weapons	Thatcham Bray Iver Denham	Holocene (c.10 000 to 5500 BP)
	LATE PALAEOLITHIC	Blades Leaf-points Small tools	Uxbridge Goring Avington	Late Devensian (Oxygen Isotope Stage 2)
EARLY PALAEOLITHIC	MOUSTERIAN OF ACHEULIAN TRADITION	Flake-blades Flake tools Flat-butted cordate hand-axes	Acton	Early Devensian (Oxygen Isotope Stage 5d to 5a)
	LEVALLOISIAN	Flake-blades Prepared cores Flake tools Some hand-axes	Northfleet West Drayton Crayford	Wolstonian (Oxygen Isotope stages ?8 to 6)
	ACHEULIAN	Hand-axes Flake tool	Caversham Furze Platt Swanscombe	Late Anglian to Wolstonian (Oxygen Isotope stages 12 to ?9)
	CLACTONIAN	Cores Flakes Flake tools	Clacton-on-Sea Swanscombe Little Thurrock	Late Anglian to Wolstonian (Oxygen Isotope stages 12 to?9)

some places, the flints are rolled and worn and have clearly been derived from some distance, or reworked from an older deposit. Elsewhere, as at Furze Platt, Maidenhead, they occur in a very fresh, sharp condition. At some of the richer sites, such as Swanscombe, numerous mammal bones are found with the artefacts, suggesting that the hunters butchered their prey there. Some flint tools have been found in the deposits of the late Anglian Black Park Terrace, but the gravels of the Boyn Hill and Lynch Hill terraces of the Middle Thames, and the equivalent Orsett Heath and Corbets Tey gravels of the Lower Thames, have yielded the greatest number. They are rare in the Taplow Terrace gravels, where they usually occur in an abraded condition, suggesting derivation from earlier deposits. They are even rarer in the younger gravels of the various 'Floodplain' terraces.

Some flint implements have been found in place, buried on actual land surfaces that have survived successive periods of erosion and weathering; for example at Crayford, 'brickearth' overlies an undisturbed working floor of flint tools and broken mammal bones. Similar sites are known at West Drayton, Acton, Stoke Newington and other parts of north-east London. There is also an area high on the North Downs at Kingswood Common, near

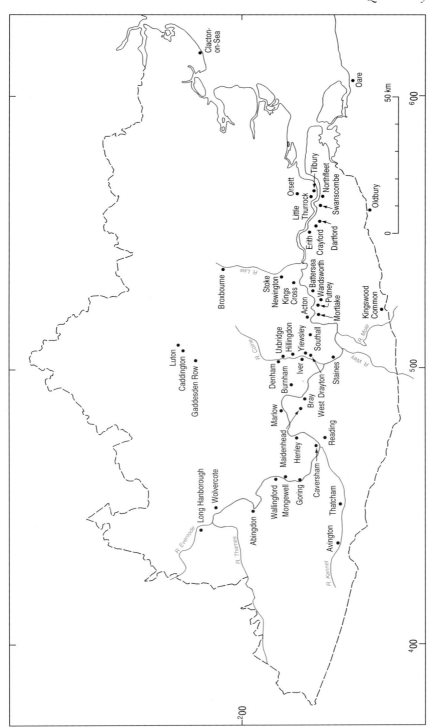

Figure 34 Sketch map showing the locations of Stone Age sites mentioned in the text.

Banstead, where Palaeolithic flint tools are found on the present ground surface, having escaped the erosion that swept the material from other sites into the valley gravels. Similarly, an important group of sites high on the Chilterns, around Luton, Caddington and at Gaddesden Row, yields hand-axes and other artefacts lying on a former land surface, now buried beneath slope deposits. Their discoverer was able to rejoin many of the flint flakes left by the toolmakers, proving that the material lay where it had been discarded.

The most characteristic artefact of the **Acheulian Industry** (and indeed of the Early Palaeolithic) is the hand-axe, a sharp-edged implement of pointed or rounded form, generally 100 to 200 mm long with a heavy butt (Plate 21). This was probably a general-purpose tool, especially useful for dismembering and skinning large animals. Hand axes were made by striking flakes from a suitable nodule or lump of flint, using another flint or quartzite pebble as a hammerstone, and were often finished with softer hammers of bone or antler. Freshly made, the edges of a hand-axe would have been razor sharp, but when found in river gravels they are usually dulled by rolling and abrasion and their surfaces may be stained brown or yellow by iron compounds from the deposit. The first hand-axe documented anywhere in the world was found in gravel near Kings Cross in London, at the end of the seventeenth century. The Thames valley can also claim the largest hand-axe in Europe, a magnificent specimen, 320 mm long, from Furze Platt, Maidenhead.

Various groups of hand-axe types have been identified and appear to represent different traditions, but there is no reliable correlation between their degree of refinement and the passage of time. However, there is one group of very crudely made hand-axes, that some archaeologists consider may belong to an early period; such hand-axes have been found at West Drayton and Yiewsley. Some of the Acheulian groups, probably the later ones, contain very elegant scrapers (Plate 21), such as are found in the upper levels of Rickson's Pit at Swanscombe.

In the Upper Thames valley, hand-axes have been found in gravels near Wallingford, and at least one is known from the Hanborough Terrace at Long Hanborough (Plate 18). These may constitute the earliest Acheulian industries in the region. In the Middle Thames valley, there are many sites with rich concentrations of hand-axes, particularly in the Reading and Maidenhead–Burnham areas. Hand-axes occur in abundance within the 'Ancient Channel' between Caversham and Henley (Figure 34), a section of the former course of the Thames, infilled with gravels of the Black Park Terrace.

Plate 21   Palaeolithic implements

1   Clactonian pebble chopper-core. Clacton-on-Sea.
2   Clactonian flake with secondary working. Clacton-on-Sea.
3 a–b   Levalloisian 'Tortoise core', Baker's Hole, Northfleet. The shape of the large flake which has been removed from this core can be seen in the plan view.
4 a–b   Cordate hand-axe, sharpened by a final tranchet blow from near the tip. Upper Loam, Barnfield Pit, Swanscombe.
5   Side-scraper made on a thick flake retaining much of its cortex. Upper Gravel, Rickson's Pit, Swanscombe.
6 a–b   Pointed hand-axe made of bi-zoned flint. Middle Gravel, Barnfield Pit, Swanscombe. (*Drawings by J J Wymer*)

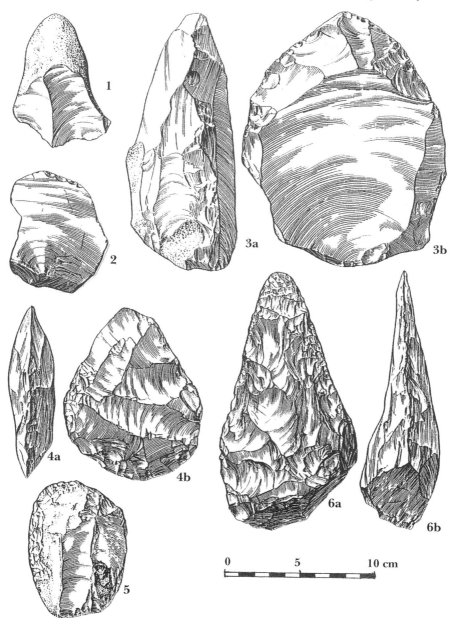

They also occur in smaller numbers in correlative gravels at Hillingdon. Much of the West End of London is built on Lynch Hill Gravel and hand-axes have been found at several localities between Oxford Street and Piccadilly. In the Lower Thames, there are a number of Palaeolithic sites between Dartford and Northfleet, mainly associated with the Orsett Heath Gravel. Swanscombe offers the best archaeological sequence, with industries of mainly pointed hand-axes in gravels in the lower part of the section, and mainly cordate or ovate forms (Plate 21) in the overlying loam. The famous Swanscombe Skull came from the upper part of the gravels in Barnfield pit (Plate 22) and was associated with a varied mammal fauna. The front of the skull (probably a woman's) is missing, but it is considered to represent an archaic form of *Homo sapiens*, although the exceptionally thick bone and other features suggest affinities with the Neanderthal people. It is the only human skull in Europe to be directly associated with a hand-axe industry, and dates from the Swanscombe interglacial (Oxygen Isotope Stage 11) (Tables 9 and 10).

The **Clactonian Industry** was very simple, concentrating on the production of fairly large and thick flakes that could be used as they were or further trimmed into scrapers, borers or other tools. They were struck from cores, some of which were probably used as choppers (Plate 21). This 'Chopper/chopper-core tradition' is found over much of the Old World in the early and middle part of

Plate 22   Barnfield Pit, Swanscombe, Kent. This famous pit is excavated in the deposits of the Orsett Heath (or Boyn Hill) Gravel of the River Thames. The photograph was taken in 1937, at the time of the discovery of the Swanscombe Skull, which was found at the level marked by the labels (A70790).

the Pleistocene Period. At the type site at Clacton-on-Sea, the industry occurs in deposits mainly of Swanscombe interglacial age. It is well represented in the fluviatile clays, sands and gravels once exposed at the base of the cliffs west of Clacton pier, and on the nearby foreshore. It is associated with a fauna of ox or bison, red and fallow deer, horse, straight-tusked elephant and rhinoceros. Mollusc and pollen types indicate conditions of an open river with surrounding woodland and swamp, but the occupation was probably spread over a long period with varying environments. Micro-wear analysis of some of the flakes shows that Clactonian people were working wood, cutting meat and scraping hides. Excavations to the west have uncovered the same flint industry, probably from an occupation of a slightly earlier period, ranging from the latter part of the preceding Anglian cold phase.

A very similar flint industry and fauna is found at Swanscombe, underlying the Acheulian hand-axe industries. The industry is also found in the Anglian gravels of the 'Ancient Channel' between Caversham and Henley, in association with other hand-axe industries. There is a further rich Clactonian site in Corbets Tey Gravel at Little Thurrock, Essex.

The **Levalloisian Industry** is characterised by well-formed flake tools. Large, serviceable flakes were produced by a process involving the elaborate preparation of a flint core to predetermine the shape of the flake, which was removed with one final blow. A long core would produce a long flake, a round core a round flake, and so on. The waste product is the 'tortoise core', named on account of its shape (Plate 21). The production method called for high skill from the maker and a plentiful supply of good-quality flint. Some archaeologists think that the Acheulian flint knappers adapted this technique when they had access to such supplies, and thus prefer to regard the Levalloisian Industry merely as a variant of the Acheulian.

The earliest-known Levalloisian artefacts in Britain are probably those from Purfleet. These were found in early Wolstonian, cold climate gravels, that overlie interglacial sediments thought to date from Oxygen Isotope Stage 9. At West Thurrock and Crayford, Levalloisian implements have been found in somewhat younger gravels, beneath interglacial sediments probably dating from Stage 7. The site at Crayford was used for the production of flake-blades. When excavated in the late nineteenth century, some of the flakes were reassembled into the shape of the original nodule, and for many years formed an impressive exhibit in the former Geological Museum in South Kensington.

The Baker's Hole site at Northfleet has yielded the richest Levalloisian material in Britain. The flint artefacts are buried beneath coombe deposits that accumulated under periglacial conditions, suggesting a very barren landscape immediately after, and possibly during, the human occupation of the area. The lack of vegetational cover on the Chalk slopes probably left large quantities of fresh flint exposed as raw material for the Levalloisian craftsmen.

The **Mousterian Industry of Acheulian tradition** is represented at Creffield Road, Acton, where large numbers of Levalloisian flakes were found in association with a few hand-axes of flat-butted, cordate form. The flints were found deep in 'brickearth' that overlies terrace gravel, the latter probably relating to the Lynch Hill Terrace. The 'brickearth' probably includes Devensian loess deposits, and this is likely to be the date of the industry at Acton. Many of the flakes from the Acton site are of a distinctive pointed form, made by the Levalloisian technique. Such a flake was found beside the skeleton of a mammoth at Southall in the nineteenth century, and it seems probable that it was used as a spearhead.

A series of small hand-axes belonging to this industry were found at Oldbury, Kent, in deposits that appear to have once underlain a rock shelter. This would be a typical situation for such an industry on mainland Europe, where it is associated with Neanderthal people. Other flat-butted, cordate hand-axes have been dredged from the Thames at Putney, Wandsworth, Erith and Tilbury. One was found beneath the silt of a low terrace, at Marlow in Buckinghamshire.

Late Palaeolithic industries

The Late Palaeolithic period includes the glacial maximum of the Devensian Stage, when sea level was perhaps 120 m lower than at present and Britain was joined to continental Europe. Palaeolithic people probably continued to inhabit the valleys at this time, but their sites are rarely exposed; many were probably destroyed or buried by fluvial deposits as sea level rose at the end of the Devensian. However, a leaf point was discovered in gravels overlying the 'arctic plant bed' at Broxbourne in the Lea valley, and some shouldered flint points from Oare, Kent, are of Late Palaeolithic type. A rich site of this age has recently been found at Uxbridge.

Mesolithic and Neolithic industries

As the climate ameliorated early in the Holocene, hunters exploited the herds of red deer that migrated into Britain from the continent; Britain did not finally become an island until perhaps about 8000 years BP. The most favoured areas for occupation were the margins of the swampy regions of the tributaries of the Thames, particularly the Kennet, Colne, Mole, Wey and Lea, where remains of Mesolithic (Middle Stone Age) camps have been found beneath peat, tufa or alluvium. Later, Mesolithic people began to inhabit the more open landscape, such as the chalk downs, as well as the river valleys.

The most characteristic Mesolithic artefacts are tiny pointed flints known as microliths, that were sometimes inserted into the tips and sides of spears and arrows, and also used as drill points. At Wandsworth and Battersea, barbed points of antler have been dredged from the Thames, together with numerous distinctive, 'tranchet'-type, flint axe-heads, sharpened by transverse flaking across the cutting end.

Neolithic (New Stone Age) immigrants arrived long after Britain had become separated from the continent by the last rise of sea level. The River Thames appears to have been an important route, and they established causewayed enclosures at Orsett, Staines and Abingdon. Their finely made, ground and polished stone and flint axe-heads have frequently been dredged out of the Thames, and Late Neolithic pottery vessels have come from Mortlake in London and Mongewell, Oxfordshire. Apart from a thin cover of silt or mud, Neolithic remains generally lie on the present ground surface. One important exception is in the Lower Thames valley, where a considerable thickness of alluvium has accumulated since Neolithic times in response to a rising sea level. A human skull of this date was found deep in the alluvium during the construction of Tilbury Docks.

10   Geology and man

Much of the geology discussed so far in this guide has been concerned with the ancient history of the region, but this chapter deals with aspects of the science that are of crucial importance to our everyday lives. Virtually all fuels and raw materials for industry are obtained, directly or indirectly, from natural deposits, and a knowledge of geology is fundamental in mineral prospecting and extraction. Much of the world's drinking water is pumped from rock strata, and an understanding of hydrogeological processes is essential for the proper utilisation and conservation of groundwater resources. Some knowledge of geological processes and of the physical properties of geological formations is also important for those involved in the construction industry.

MINERAL RESOURCES

The most valuable mineral resources of the region are those used by the construction industry, notably sand and gravel, brick clay and cement-making materials. The rapid growth of London and other urban centres, from the nineteenth century onwards, created great demands for these products, most of which were met from within the region. In the twentieth century, their extraction has tended to become concentrated on fewer, larger sites (Figure 35). Such operations often have a future value as landfill sites, or in the case of flooded workings, may become wildlife conservation areas or be developed for water sports.

Sand and gravel

Economically, sand and gravel is by far the most important mineral product of the region, with an average annual output of about 16 million tonnes in the 1990s, of which Essex contributed about 25 per cent. Although usually grouped together, sand and gravel are separate commodities, and in the extraction industry, the term 'gravel' is applied to material with a predominance of clasts over 5 mm in diameter, and 'sand' describes finer material. Gravel provides an important source of aggregate for concrete, mortar and asphalt products, because the region is deficient in sources of hard rock suitable for this purpose. Sand has many uses, but the greatest volume is used in the construction industry.

The main sand and gravel resources of the region are Quaternary fluvial deposits that occur beneath the alluvium of the flood plains, and form river terraces on the valley sides. The physical properties of sand and gravel reflect

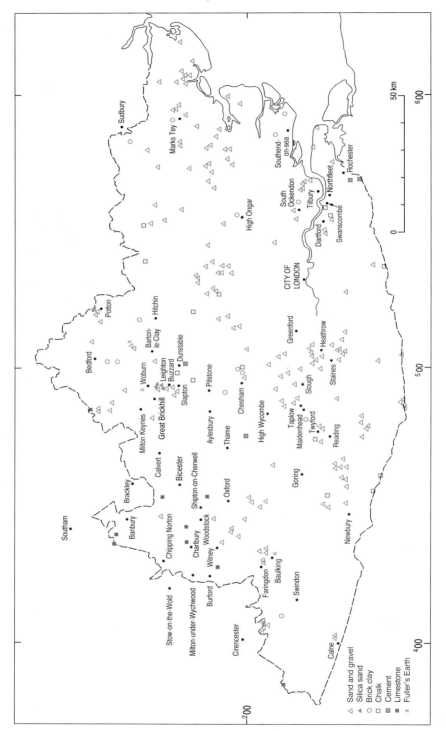

Figure 35   Sketch map showing current (1993) sites of mineral extraction.

those of the source rocks from which they were derived but, during their transport by water, many of the less durable materials are worn away, and finer particles are removed in suspension. Thus, fluvial gravels may be notably better for use in industry than the parent rocks.

Suballuvial gravels are normally wet-worked, producing clean aggregates ready for sale after size grading. Small operations occur in the valleys of the Ouse and the Ivel, but the main workings are concentrated in the valleys of the Thames and its major tributaries, the Colne, Lea, Kennet, Blackwater and Wey. The gravels of the Thames show a progressive downstream variation in composition, reflecting the geology of the rocks over which the river flows. At its source near Cirencester, the gravel is made up entirely of Jurassic limestone clasts, but the proportion drops to 50 per cent at Goring, with the rest of the gravel being made up of flint, quartz and ironstone. Downstream from Goring, the proportion of limestone falls markedly, with flint, derived from the Chalk, becoming the dominant component. Quartz and quartzite, derived from the more ancient, high-level gravels of the Chilterns, occur with flints in the Middle Thames gravels between Reading and Slough. Flint is the major component in the catchment of the River Kennet, which meets the Thames at Reading, and clasts of sandstone and chert originating from the Lower Greensand of the Weald may comprise up to 25 per cent of the gravels of the Blackwater, Loddon and Wey tributaries. Along the Ouse, limestone and quartzite clasts are dominant. The Kesgrave Sands and Gravels of Essex, the deposits of the ancestral Thames, typically contain few fines, and so are a valuable resource. These gravels are characterised by flint, quartz and quartzite clasts with minor chert and volcanic rocks. Locally they are worked for specialist uses, including water filtration sands.

Glaciofluvial sands and gravels occur extensively in the northern part of the region, but are very variable in composition. In contrast to the fluvial sands and gravels, they may have excessive proportions of fines and chalk, which may render them fit only for use as 'hoggin', a fill material used in road-building and suchlike. The main clasts in the gravel include flint, quartzite, quartz, limestone and sandstone, igneous rocks and chalk. They provide a source of aggregate in Essex; at some sites, they rest upon the Kesgrave Sands and Gravels, and both deposits may be exploited in conjunction.

The solid formations also provide important resources of sand and fine aggregates, the most notable being the Woburn Sand Formation of Bedfordshire. This formation shows considerable local variation in grain-size and purity, yielding sands for many different purposes around Leighton Buzzard and near Potton. The purer and coarser sands in the upper part of the formation are mainly used for water filtration, concrete tile manufacture, and foundry moulding sand. The lower part of the formation provides mainly building and fine concreting sand.

The Corallian Group near Faringdon in Oxfordshire, and the Lower Greensand at Faringdon and near Calne in Wiltshire, are worked on a modest scale for building sand. The Thanet Sand Formation has been worked in Essex, often by deepening pits dug in Quaternary sands and gravels. These sands are rather fine grained and have been used for fill in motorway construction and, at Linford near Tilbury, in the manufacture of lightweight building blocks. They were formerly worked as a moulding sand. Moulding sand has also been obtained from the Whitchurch Sand Formation near Oxford and also at Stone near Aylesbury, where pure silica sand for glass manufacture was worked until the 1960s.

Brick clay

In past centuries, virtually all the clay formations of the region were utilised on a small scale for brick-making, but mechanisation in the latter part of the nineteenth century meant that production became concentrated at fewer, larger sites.

Currently, the major source of brick clay in the region is the Peterborough Member of the Oxford Clay Formation. Its use for brick manufacture on a large commercial scale was pioneered in the 1880s at Fletton, near Peterborough in Cambridgeshire. An important characteristic, on which its economic importance is based, is its high carbon content (about 5 per cent). This burns off during firing and substantially reduces the energy costs of brick manufacture. The clay also has a comparatively high natural moisture content which allows it to be pressed into moulds without the addition of water. The Peterborough Member was worked until recently at Calvert and Newton Longville, near Milton Keynes, but now only the large Stewartby works and the smaller Kempston works, both near Bedford, survive. These two sites, together with those near Peterborough in Cambridgeshire, supplied about a quarter of Britain's brick output in 1991. Although generally less suitable for brick-making, the higher parts of the Oxford Clay Formation were formerly worked at Purton near Swindon (Plate 6), and at many sites near Oxford, including Woodham, which survived until the 1960s.

The Kimmeridge Clay Formation was also worked for brick-making. Around Oxford and Aylesbury, the sandy upper beds of the formation were particularly favoured, because the quartz content helped to prevent shrinkage on firing. At Swindon, Kimmeridge Clay was extensively worked during the town's rapid expansion as a railway centre in the last century. The Gault Formation was also used, most notably around Thame, north-east of Oxford, where it was worked until the 1940s. Until recently, a brickworks at Arlesey, near Hitchin in Bedfordshire utilised this formation to produce yellow facing bricks.

In general, the London Clay does not meet modern standards for brick-making, because of its high smectite content which causes excessive shrinkage and distortion during drying and firing. However, hand-made bricks are made near Sudbury, in Essex. It was more widely used in the past; the vast numbers of bricks used to build the expanding London suburbs in the nineteenth century, were the product of weathered London Clay blended with street sweepings of grit and cinder.

Weathered clays of the Reading Formation are worked in small brickworks near Chesham, Buckinghamshire, and near Maidenhead, in Berkshire (Figure 35), for facing bricks and roof tiles. In Essex, loessic 'brickearth' loams, associated with river terrace deposits, form the basis of a small-scale brick industry near Southend-on-Sea, and lacustrine clays at Marks Tey are used to manufacture drainage pipes and facing bricks.

Clays are now also in demand for the lining and sealing of landfill sites to protect aquifers and rivers from leachate pollution. At High Ongar in Essex, the London Clay is worked for the production of lightweight aggregates, used principally in making building blocks, and for floor and roof screeds. The clay expands on calcining at 1200°C, to give a lightweight aggregate which is fire resistant, and has good heat- and sound-insulation properties.

Chalk and clay for cement manufacture

Prior to the nineteenth century, building construction had been based on lime mortars. The invention of Portland cement, which sets even when submerged, revolutionised the construction industry and made possible the large-scale civil engineering works of the nineteenth century. Portland cement is a complex mixture of calcium silicates and aluminates. It is manufactured by combining calcareous and argillaceous raw materials at high temperature. Strict control of the composition of the mix is essential, to maintain correct and uniform quality of the end product.

The cement industry originated in the mid-nineteenth century, with production centred on the Chalk outcrops flanking the Thames estuary and the River Medway. The availability of raw materials, proximity to major markets and easy transport links by road, rail and water were important factors in the location of the industry. The region is still important for cement manufacture, despite a recent decline in the use of chalk as a raw material. The chalk is mixed with clayey material in the ratio of about 4 to 1 and calcined in a rotary kiln at 1400 to 1500°C. The argillaceous component may be brought in from distant quarries or, where possible, from different levels in the same quarry; the Lower Chalk is often used in this way. The resultant clinker is ground with a small proportion of gypsum, which controls the setting time of the cement product.

The cement works at Northfleet, in north Kent, is one of the largest in Britain, with an output of 0.75 million tonnes in 1993. It utilises locally quarried Upper Chalk, which is mixed with London Clay from South Ockendon, in Essex. This is slurried and pumped to Northfleet via a pipeline beneath the Thames. In the Medway valley, near Rochester, and at Chinnor in Oxfordshire, Lower and Middle Chalk are quarried for cement-making and these beds were also used at Pitstone, in Buckinghamshire, until 1991. Kensworth Quarry, near Dunstable, exploits Middle and Upper Chalk, which is slurried and pumped through a pipeline, some 80km long, to works at Rugby and Southam in Warwickshire. There, after mixing with clayey material from the Lower Jurassic 'Blue Lias', it is made into cement. Middle Jurassic limestones were used for cement manufacture at Shipton-on-Cherwell, near Oxford, until the mid-1980s.

Flint

Flint occurs abundantly as nodules and tabular sheets in the Middle and Upper Chalk. It is produced as a by-product of chalk working for cement at Northfleet (see above). The flints are used as grinding media to slurry the chalk and are subsequently recovered, washed and graded. Those over 125 mm diameter are used for 'knapping' or splitting for decorative masonry and flooring. Flints in the 50 to 100 mm size range are used, after calcination and grinding, as a white filler in earthenware manufacture. Finer sizes are crushed to give a range of grades, used in non-skid, abrasion- and acid-resistant flooring, and exposed aggregate finishes. Crushed flint is also used as an abrasive for stone cutting and grit blasting, and for water filtration.

Rock aggregate and lime

The Jurassic limestones of the north-western part of the region are the only major sources of hard rock locally. Production is now based mainly on the Great Oolite Group, particularly the White Limestone Formation, which supplies constructional fill and agricultural lime. The Marlstone Rock Formation is also still worked on a small scale for fill. In the past, both the Clypeus Grit (Inferior Oolite Group) and the Cornbrash Formation (at the top of the Great Oolite Group), provided rubble that was used for road-making.

The pure chalks of the Middle and Upper Chalk are valued for their whiteness and reflectivity. Chalk from Pinden, near Dartford in Kent, is processed at Swanscombe to produce a finely powdered filler for paper, paint, rubber and plastics. A major part of this output is supplied in slurry form to local paper mills, where it reduces the cost and enhances the printing quality of the paper. In the Chilterns, a number of small quarries produce crushed chalk for agricultural lime and construction fill.

Fuller's earth

Fuller's earth is an unusual type of clay, rich in the mineral calcium smectite (montmorillonite), which results from the decomposition of volcanic ash in marine environments. Smectites have a layered molecular structure similar to micas, but with loosely held, exchangable cations, such as calcium, magnesium and sodium. This structure is responsible for the absorbency, high cation-exchange capacity, swelling characteristics, and water-sealing properties of fuller's earth, on which its various applications are based.

Fuller's earth derives its name from its use in the cleansing and de-greasing ('fulling') of wool. This was its principal application until the latter part of the nineteenth century. It was originally worked for this purpose near Bath, to the west of the region, from a part of the Great Oolite succession which consequently became known as the Fuller's Earth Formation, although true fuller's earths occur only very locally within it. Currently, commercial deposits of fuller's earth, usually containing at least 80 to 85 per cent of calcium smectite, are worked from the Lower Greensand near Woburn (Plate 23) and Clophill, Bedfordshire, and at Baulking in Oxfordshire. The fuller's earth occurs in lenticular seams, rarely up to about 3.5 m thick. Natural and processed fuller's earth has many uses in civil engineering, and is also used for bonding foundry sands, refining edible oils, in paper-making and as a pet litter. The total British output of fuller's earth in 1993 was 187 000 tonnes, of which the major part came from the three sites in the region.

Coal, oil and gas

The presence of concealed Coal Measures at depth beneath Oxfordshire, was first proved in 1875 by a borehole at Burford. Geological Survey boreholes drilled between 1960 and 1973 near Witney, Bicester and Banbury, provided

Plate 23 Extraction of fuller's earth from the Woburn Sands Formation (Lower Greensand), Old Wavendon Heath, Bedfordshire. The fuller's earth forms a seam up to about 3 m thick at the bottom of the quarry. Working entails the removal of up to 40 m of sand overburden which is dumped in the worked-out area (left) as the face advances (A15114).

more information on the distribution of the deposits. The thickest succession was proved at Apley Barn near Witney (Chapter 2; Figure 6), which penetrated Coal Measures between depths of 250 and 1210 m. Two coal seams exceed 1.4m in thickness, and the total combined thickness of coals is 8.8 m. Generally, however, individual seams are rather thin. Subsequently, further boreholes and seismic surveys by British Coal proved that the Coal Measures extend southwards nearly as far as Newbury, in Berkshire (Figures 4 and 6), although here the deposits lie at greater depth, and the coal seams are thinner and of poorer quality.

No attempt has been made to mine the Berkshire and Oxfordshire coals and, given the dramatic contraction of the industry in the 1990s, there seems little probability that they will be worked within the foreseeable future. Minor traces of methane gas were noted during the drilling of some boreholes, but this is unlikely to be of commercial interest because the coals have a very low gas content compared with seams in many other parts of Britain.

A number of oil and gas exploration boreholes have been drilled in various parts of the region, but no commercial discoveries have been made, and the general lack of suitable source rocks in the region indicates low prospectivity. In the 1960s, the Triassic Sherwood Sandstone Group, present at depth between Brackley and Chipping Norton, was considered for use as a natural storage reservoir for gas produced elsewhere. Many investigation boreholes were drilled through the Trias before the scheme was abandoned.

Iron ore

Although ferruginous minerals are fairly widely distributed in the Mesozoic rocks of the region, only the Marlstone Rock Formation (Middle Lias), has been worked commercially. It was first worked at Fawler, near Charlbury in Oxfordshire, between 1858 and 1887, where the iron ore was about 2.4 m thick. Later workings were concentrated in the Wroxton–Bloxham area, near Banbury, where it attains a thickness of 10 m; the ore was worked in large quarries below thin overburden. The iron ore comprises mainly shelly, partly oolitic limestone with iron present as the minerals siderite, berthierine and limonite. It contains up to 25 per cent iron, but is of low grade by present world standards; this and other economic factors led to the demise of the workings in 1967.

The Marlstone was worked mainly to supply iron and steel works in South Wales. The availability of rail transport was an important factor in its exploitation. Total production during the period 1940 to 1967 was about 33 million tonnes. It has also been worked as a building stone and as hardcore, and is still extracted for the latter purpose. The fines produced in crushing the rock were used as a flux for iron smelting in South Wales until recently.

Phosphate

Locally produced phosphate rock was formerly an important raw material for fertiliser manufacture. During the late nineteenth century, phosphatic nodules and pebbles ('coprolites'), were extracted for this purpose from several horizons in the Cretaceous rocks of the region. The main horizons worked include the basal Woburn Sands, near Great Brickhill in Buckinghamshire, the Upper Gault, at several localities between Thame in Oxfordshire and Slapton in Buckinghamshire, the Cambridge Greensand, north-east of Barton-le-Clay in Bedfordshire and thence into Cambridgeshire, and the Red Crag in Essex. After washing, the 'coprolites' were ground and treated with sulphuric acid, to produce superphosphate fertiliser. After its brief boom, the industry declined rapidly due to competition from high-grade phosphate from overseas, and the local phosphatic deposits are no longer of economic interest.

Beds at the top of the Upper Chalk at Taplow, in Buckinghamshire, were investigated as a possible source of phosphate, when the First and Second World Wars curtailed supplies from overseas. They were never worked commercially. The phosphatic chalk contains between 7 and 15 per cent phosphorus (as P_2O_5). Lower-grade phosphatic chalks also occur around Winterbourne and Boxford, near Newbury in Berkshire.

Building stone

Generally, the region is poorly endowed with building stones, and most of the materials used have been imported from outside the region. Nevertheless, the Jurassic rocks of the north-western part have yielded some attractive limestones, including fine freestones, which were much prized by architects such as Inigo Jones, Christopher Wren and Thomas Archer. In shallow quarries, these limestones tend to be weathered and broken by joints, and so the best freestone was generally obtained from beneath a thick overburden, and often from mines. When freshly excavated from depth, such stone is relatively soft and easily worked, and can be readily sawn into blocks. It hardens slowly on exposure to the weather.

In the Banbury area, the Marlstone Rock Formation provides a pleasant rust-brown stone, which gives a distinctive character to the villages there. From Norman times, builders exploited stones from the Great Oolite Group to produce the architectural wealth of the Cotswold villages. The Chipping Norton Limestone was particularly favoured around its type area in Oxfordshire, and the Taynton Limestone was much used around Burford, and to the west. In the seventeenth and eighteenth centuries, Taynton Limestone was used in the colleges of Oxford University, and in the rebuilding of London after the Great Fire of 1666. Vast quantities were used for St Paul's Cathedral; this was obtained from quarries near Burford, owned by Wren's master mason Kit Kempster. The same stone was extensively used by John Vanburgh in the building of Blenheim Palace. Taynton Limestone was worked until quite recently at Taynton itself, and is still quarried at Farmington just west of the region. The White Limestone Formation does not generally yield durable building stone but, in the past, even-grained oolites were worked at Burford and Milton-under-Wychwood. Today, an attractive reconstituted stone is manufactured near Burford. The limestones of the Forest Marble Formation have been widely worked for rough walling stone, and a shelly ragstone facies from the Woodstock area, known as Bladon Stone, is combined with other freestones as a structural and textural contrast in some Oxford buildings. The name 'Forest Marble' derives from the former use of the oyster-rich limestones as polished slabs for fireplaces and stairs. Fissile, flaggy limestones from this formation have been used for paving and roofing tiles, and they are still worked for this purpose to the south of Burford. Similar 'tilestones' were obtained from the Fuller's Earth Formation in the Windrush valley in the same area, and were worked as 'Cotswold Slates' from approximately the same horizon near Stow-on-the-Wold, to the west of the region. However, the best-quality roofing stone was obtained from the 'Stonesfield Slate', which occurs as several thin seams within the Taynton Limestone. It was worked from an extensive network of adits, shafts and galleries, beneath the village of Stonesfield, near Charlbury, and in its immediate neighbourhood.

Many of the older buildings in Oxford, notably the city walls and New College Bell Tower, are built of local 'Coral Rag' and Wheatley Limestone from the Corallian Group. These rubbly, shelly limestones were extensively quarried around Headington, now in the eastern suburbs of Oxford, and were used continuously until the seventeenth century.

The Portland and Purbeck formations between Oxford and Aylesbury, provide soft, cream-coloured limestones which were extensively used in local churches and villages. The small outcrop of these beds at Swindon has also been utilised in the same way. However, the white Portland Stone seen in the buildings of London and many other towns, has all been imported into the region from the Isle of Portland in Dorset.

The distinctive dark brown, limonite-cemented 'Carstone' from the Woburn Sand Formation around Leighton Buzzard contributes to the character of Bedfordshire buildings. To the south-east, the Totternhoe Stone, in the Lower Chalk, has been used in building since Norman times, encouraging carving and decorative work in architecture, as seen in Dunstable Priory. Recently, working has been resumed to provide material for the restoration of local buildings. Throughout the Chilterns and North Downs, flints from local chalk pits have been used in both simple buildings and, on a grander scale, in the churches of the area. The irregular nodules are used in rubble walling, and elaborate patterning is created with squared and knapped flints contained between stone dressings.

The sarsen sandstones of the chalk downlands have been widely used for building; examples can be seen in the structure of Windsor Castle. This material probably came from Walter's Ash or Denner Hill, near High Wycombe, where sarsens were worked until the late nineteenth century for paving setts and kerbstones. The pebbly Hertfordshire Puddingstone, a variant of sarsen, is an unusual building material confined largely to south Hertfordshire. It was used chiefly by Norman and medieval builders, who relied upon local materials when transport from distant sources was difficult.

In the heart of the London Basin, there is a dearth of high-quality building stone, but an interesting variety of substitutes has been used. Rounded flint pebbles, from terrace gravels, figure prominently in buildings along the valleys of the Thame and its tributaries, notably the Colne. Septarian cementstone nodules from the London Clay, discarded by the brick-makers or gathered from the fields, were used locally for walling in Essex; they were also roasted to make lime mortars. Possibly the most distinctive of the local materials are ferricretes, variously called 'puddingstone', 'ironstone' or 'carstone'. They are limonite-cemented gravels and sands, formed by groundwaters rich in iron. The terrace gravels of the Thames floodplain were the main source of ferricretes; they are best seen in the Norman churches around Heathrow, Greenford and Staines. Flints, septaria and ferricretes were usually framed and strengthened in buildings by quoins, string-courses and lintels of either Kentish Ragstone (Lower Greensand) from the Medway valley, or the softer Reigate Stone (Upper Greensand) from northern Surrey. These stones were often replaced by Bath Stone (Great Oolite) by Victorian restorers.

Within the City of London, Kentish Ragstone and Reigate Stone have been the mainstay of the more substantial buildings since Roman times, when it was used in the walls of Londinium. Later, the Normans used large quantities to build the Tower of London, in combination with Middle Jurassic Caen Stone from Normandy.

After the Great Fire of 1666, London, as redesigned by Wren, became a showcase for Portland Stone. The stone was transported by sea in great quantities from the quarries on the Isle of Portland in Dorset. Its use was continued by Nicolas Hawksmoor and, in the nineteenth century, by John Nash. It was often used in combination with brick, or with brick rendered with a white stucco finish which characterises the squares and terraces of Bloomsbury and Belgravia. The expansion of London and the building of new parish churches saw a resurgence of the use of Kentish Ragstone, mainly from the Medway valley, and transported by barge to city wharves. Virtually all the London suburbs have a parish church of greyish buff Kentish Ragstone with yellowish brown Bath Stone dressings.

With the coming of the railways, Victorian architects such as Charles Barry and Gilbert Scott were able to utilise a wide range of new materials. Notable imports were Scottish, Irish and Cornish granites. Many more exotic stones have been used in the bank and office buildings built this century. The advent of cladding techniques, using thin slabs of natural stone over a concrete interior, has greatly widened the range of rock types utilised. Pavings in London offer yet another suite of imported rocks. Flagstones commonly include York Stone from the Coal Measures of Yorkshire, and kerbstones include diorites from Guernsey and granites from Cornwall, Leicestershire, Cumbria and Scotland. Cobbles or setts, now seen mainly in quiet mews, tend to be rich in all of these igneous rocks, together with gneisses from Scandinavia or Brittany.

HYDROGEOLOGY AND WATER SUPPLIES

The London and Thames Valley region has a high population, but relatively low rainfall, and so great stress is placed on water resources. Rivers are an important source for public supply. The Thames has a mean flow of 66 cumecs (cubic metres per second) at Teddington Weir. About 60 per cent of this flow is derived from natural groundwater discharge (baseflow), with the remainder mainly from overland flow (run-off). Water abstracted from the river is returned as treated sewage effluent and is thus recycled *en route* to the sea. Normally, some 10 per cent of the flow of the Thames is treated effluent, but this proportion may rise dramatically in times of drought. Other rivers in the region used for water supply are the Avon, Ouse, Crouch, Blackwater, Colne and Stour (Figure 3).

Direct abstraction from rivers is restricted by the need to maintain minimum acceptable flows, both for environmental and amenity reasons, and this often results in the need to augment low flows with water from reservoirs, filled when the river is high. Such pumped storage reservoirs have been constructed in the Lea valley, the Lower Thames Valley and at Farmoor near Oxford. However, the region is generally unsuitable for the construction of impounding reservoirs because of its high population density and the low topographic relief associated with impermeable strata.

The average annual rainfall is over 800 mm in the west of the region, falling to 500 mm at the Essex coast. When this rain falls on the ground surface a large proportion is lost by evaporation and transpiration by plants, particularly during the summer months, and so the 'effective rainfall' varies from some 300 mm in the west to less than 100 mm in the east. An additional portion is lost through direct run-off to streams, but the remainder seeps into the soil and, when this is saturated, into any permeable bedrock beneath. After infiltrating through the unsaturated zone, this water eventually reaches the fully saturated zone (the 'water table'), to become groundwater. Infiltration takes place predominantly in the winter months, from October to March. Once within the saturated zone, groundwater moves slowly under gravity, until it is naturally discharged at springs or along seepage lines, to contribute to the flow of rivers (baseflow).

Groundwater has been exploited for thousands of years, from springs and wells which have provided a focus for human settlement. Holywell in Shoreditch, Clerkenwell, and St Clement's Well in the Strand were three of London's main sources of drinking water for many centuries. Today, ground-water contributes more than half of the total public water supply, and is one of the region's most important natural resources.

An aquifer is defined as a permeable formation from which useful quanti-ties of groundwater may be pumped from wells and boreholes. In contrast, an aquiclude is a formation of low permeability which will not release useful quantities of groundwater; it may support groundwater in an overlying aquifer, or confine groundwater under pressure in an underlying aquifer.

Chalk aquifer

The Chalk is the most important aquifer of the region. It crops out around the margins of the London Basin and, in the centre is confined by major aquicludes in the Palaeogene succession, notably the London Clay (Figure 2). The overall pattern of groundwater flow within the London Basin commences with rainwater infiltrating into the Chalk at outcrop and thence moving under the London Clay, discharging either by slow upward leakage through the aquiclude, or into the River Thames where the aquifer is exposed in the river bed. Near the Isle of Dogs, the volume of this natural discharge was formerly so great, that ships lying in the tideway merely had to lower a bucket over the side to replenish their stocks of fresh water.

The Chalk has complex hydraulic properties. It has a porous matrix providing groundwater storage but, because the pores and their interconnec-tions are so minute, the matrix permeability and thus the speed with which water can be taken up or released, is low. This is illustrated by radiocarbon dating, which shows that the groundwater in the Chalk beneath Central London is more than 20 000 years old (since infiltration), and even close to the outcrop, a significant portion of ancient water is present.

Chalk also has a secondary porosity, due to the presence of joints and fissures. Best developed at shallow depths and beneath valleys, these fissures can provide rapid groundwater transport and contain the most mobile water. Because of these properties, the level of the water table changes rapidly in response to winter rains or summer droughts. Annual fluctuation in the water table is typically about 5 m, but it may be more than 30 m; consequently spring heads of seasonal streams (bournes) move up and down their valleys, depending on the water level in the aquifer. Pumping from a borehole depresses the water level in the borehole and the surrounding aquifer, forming a 'cone of depression'. The highly transmissive properties of fissured Chalk allow shallow but very extensive cones to develop around some boreholes, so that over-pumping may interfere with the natural flow of springs and rivers, and with other boreholes a considerable distance away.

The early development of the Chalk as an aquifer depended on hand-dug shafts, which in some cases had horizontal adits extending from them. These adits, exceptionally a kilometre or more in length, were constructed in times of drought when groundwater levels were low. Many of these ancient shaft and adit systems maintain very high pumping yields, in some cases over 6000 cubic metres per day (m^3/d). Today, groundwater development is primarily carried out by drilling boreholes. The rate at which water can be abstracted from a borehole depends both on the hydraulic properties of the aquifer, and the dimensions of the borehole. Thus the Upper and Middle Chalk tend to be more productive than the argillaceous Lower Chalk, and whereas a 150 mm-diameter borehole penetrating saturated Chalk by 30 m may yield up to 500 m^3/d, a 300 mm-diameter borehole penetrating to the same depth may yield over 2000 m^3/d.

Early in the eighteenth century, the first deep wells were sunk through the confining strata to the basal Palaeogene sands immediately above the Chalk, and later wells were sunk into the Chalk itself. Originally, the wells in central London overflowed, although the belief that the fountains in Trafalgar Square were directly powered by such artesian pressure is unfounded. Groundwater exploitation increased until, by the late 1930s, some 225 000 m^3/day were pumped. This rate of abstraction was considerably greater than the natural replenishment by infiltration at the outcrop, and the artesian wells ceased to flow. By the 1930s, groundwater levels were depressed by as much as 75 m; it has been calculated that about 1000 cubic kilometres of aquifer were dewatered. Legislation to limit pumping, accompanied by a decline in water-intensive industry, reduced groundwater abstraction, until, in the 1960s, the rate of natural replenishment overtook abstraction. By the early 1990s, groundwater levels were rising at approximately one metre per year. Some deep structures, such as the underground railway system and the foundations and basement storeys of certain high-rise buildings, which were constructed during the period of depressed levels, are now threatened by the rising water table. To avoid the obvious consequences, schemes have been prepared to control the rise, by increasing groundwater pumping in selected districts.

The main chemical characteristics of Chalk groundwater are established within a few metres of the surface, in the unsaturated zone. The acidity of infiltrating rainwater is quickly neutralised and calcium carbonate is taken into solution. The essential chemical make-up of the water changes little as it moves through the aquifer, although small quantities of elements such as magnesium, strontium and potassium, may be taken up. The groundwater is generally of the calcium-bicarbonate type. It is a very hard water, as is shown by the scale in kettles and hot water systems, and has a total hardness in the range 200 to over 400 milligrammes per litre (mg/l) as $CaCO_3$. Beneath Palaeogene cover, the hardness may fall to less than 200 mg/l, largely due to ionic exchange of calcium for sodium from the confining clays. The chloride ion concentration at outcrop is usually less than 30 mg/l (as Cl-), but in the centre of the London Basin, depressed groundwater levels have resulted in the ingress of saline water from the Thames estuary, and the chloride concentrations may reach more than 1000 mg/l. In the Lea valley and in the vicinity of Epping and Ilford, the sulphate concentrations may be more than 200 mg/l (as SO_4^{2-}), but at outcrop rarely exceed 30 mg/l. Fluoride is usually not detectable in waters at outcrop, but is often present where the Chalk is confined. For example, in the Hayes–Southall area, more than 3.0 mg/l of fluoride (as F) has been recorded.

Considerable quantities of pollutants may enter the pores of the Chalk matrix in the unsaturated zone, and reside there for many years. However, when the pollutants eventually reach the water table, they may then spread relatively quickly over large distances, due to the rapid groundwater flow through fissures. The history of nitrate pollution in the Chalk is a good example of the manner in which the aquifer initially retains a pollutant, which later arrives at abstraction wells in relatively high concentrations.

Other aquifers

The original source of the River Thames was a spring draining from Great Oolite limestones near Thames Head Bridge, south-west of Cirencester. Local groundwater abstraction has lowered the water table and the perennial head of the river has moved several kilometres farther down the valley. Boreholes in both the Great Oolite and the Inferior Oolite groups may yield up to 5000 m^3/d in north Wiltshire, but towards Oxfordshire and Buckinghamshire yields are poor. The groundwater has a moderate hardness up to 350 mg/l at outcrop, reducing to only 100 mg/l wherever the aquifers are confined by younger, poorly permeable rocks. The groundwater is generally saline, and unsuitable for public supply more than a few kilometres down-dip from the outcrop.

The limestones and calcareous sandstones of the Corallian Group are only of local significance as aquifers. Near Abingdon in Oxfordshire, sustainable borehole yields of up to 800 m^3/d have been obtained.

The Lower Greensand forms a useful aquifer at outcrop in Bedfordshire. There are several public supply boreholes that yield more than 3000 m^3/d. The water is of good chemical quality, but may be iron-rich in places. At Slough, the Chalk yielded little groundwater, and so a number of boreholes were drilled deeper into the Lower Greensand, which is present at a depth of some 300m. Individual wells yielded as much as 5000 m^3/d when they were sunk in the early 1900s, and they overflowed with a head of 2 to 3m. By the 1970s, however, the head had fallen by more than 25m, and pumping rates were reduced to protect the aquifer.

The Upper Greensand is locally important, for example around Wallingford in Oxfordshire, where wells may yield as much as 1700 m^3/d. In Berkshire, boreholes penetrating both the Lower Chalk and the Upper Greensand (the two are usually in hydraulic continuity) can be equally productive.

Between the Chalk and the London Clay, the Thanet Sand Formation and Lambeth Group are not very productive as aquifers, but are interesting from a hydrogeochemical point of view. They are often characterised by iron- and sulphate-rich waters, resulting from the oxidation of pyrite. Such waters at Epsom were valued for their supposed medicinal properties in the seventeenth and eighteenth centuries, and gave the name 'Epsom Salts' to magnesium sulphate, used as a purgative. With rising groundwater levels beneath London, the solution of the decomposed pyrite produces highly acidic waters, which may cause corrosion of buried steel and concrete structures, such as tunnels of the underground railway network. For example, near Old Street Station on the Northern Line, a sand body contained water with a pH of 3, and a sulphate concentration greater than 100 000 mg/l.

The arenaceous beds above the London Clay, comprising the Bagshot Formation, Bracklesham Beds and Barton Beds, contain little groundwater. That which does occur, typically contains much iron in solution.

Quaternary deposits contain some important groundwater resources, but yields are very variable, reflecting variations in aquifer lithology, thickness and catchment area. Yields from the Kesgrave Sands and Gravels of Essex, for example, vary from 40 to over 5000 m^3/d. Such superficial deposits are commonly in hydraulic continuity with the rivers flowing over them, and pumping from wells often induces flow from the river into the aquifer and hence to the well. Generally, therefore, the quality of the groundwater is little modified from that of rain or river water, although commonly with some enrichment in iron. However, these near-surface deposits are very vulnerable to pollution, particularly by nitrate from fertilisers.

Groundwater management

Management of groundwater resources involves the protection of both its yield and its quality. As springs and baseflow form a major part of the region's river flow, protection of groundwater reserves is important not only to maintain well-yields, but also to maintain surface water flows at acceptable levels.

Over the last two decades, considerable attention has been devoted to schemes to augment river flow during dry periods, with groundwater pumped from wells. This groundwater is piped to the nearest perennial stream, which is used as a natural aqueduct to supply centres of demand downstream. During the wet season, the wells can be rested to allow natural replenishment of the aquifer. The location of the abstraction boreholes is critical in such schemes; they must be sited to take advantage of the delay between groundwater abstraction and the reduction in discharge at natural outlets. A site too close to the river reduces the baseflow of the river, and may even induce return flows from the river to the borehole. The Thames Groundwater Scheme, which became operational in 1976, was the first major project of its kind in the country. Centred on the Lambourn catchment in Berkshire, pumping from 33 boreholes in the Chalk can provide 80 000 m^3/day to supplement river flow. Further development of this scheme has been hampered by the difficulty of predicting the long-term, sustainable yield of the boreholes, due to natural fluctuations in the water table related to climate, and because of the changing hydraulic properties of the aquifer with depth.

Similar principles apply to the management of wetlands and the headwaters of rivers in drought conditions. Prolonged drought, coupled with local pumping, may depress the water table beneath rivers and wetlands which will then dry out, with possibly major environmental consequences. The dry winters of 1989 to 1992 severely affected the River Darent in Kent, the Misbourne in Buckinghamshire and the Ver in Hertfordshire. An overall reduction in groundwater abstraction, coupled with local augmentation of river flow from boreholes, helped to mitigate the problem.

Artificial recharge can be used to augment a groundwater reservoir, as an alternative to constructing large surface reservoirs. In the Lea valley, a scheme conceived in the 1950s utilises the vacant storage in the Chalk aquifer by injecting excess surface water through wells. Recent drilling of additional abstraction/recharge boreholes has increased the yield to 90 000 m^3/d.

Pollution within the region provides a major challenge to those involved in groundwater management. Dense settlement and extensive industrial development in the region generate huge quantities of waste, much of which is disposed of in landfills, posing a potential threat to underlying aquifers. Intensive agriculture inevitably results in the movement of fertilisers and pesticides into groundwater. Deterioration of groundwater quality may be slow, but by the time it is noticed, much of the aquifer may have been polluted. Remediation, if feasible, will then be difficult and costly. Policy documents published by the National Rivers Authority, cover many types of pollution threat to groundwater. The application of these policies is particularly important in this region, due to the critical role that groundwater plays in its social and economic development.

GEOLOGICAL HAZARDS AND FACTORS AFFECTING DEVELOPMENT

London, with its suburbs, spreads across much of the London Basin, where geological factors have played a significant role in development. The original settlement of Londinium, in the area of the City, and the subsequent expansion of London from Roman times to the seventeenth century, took place in areas of easily developed land close to the river, but usually on river terrace gravels and not on the alluvial ground which was generally marshy and prone to flooding. Pressure on space increased dramatically from the eighteenth century through to the present, with the consequent necessity for urban spread into geologically less suitable areas.

The need to retain green-belt land around the main urban centres and the greater consideration of environmental factors, necessitate that future development will concentrate mainly on urban regeneration and utilisation of derelict land. The Docklands scheme is an example of this type of redevelopment. Such projects require a good understanding both of the natural geology of the site, and also the effects of human influence, such as the presence of made ground and contaminated land.

Tunnelling

The London Clay provides an excellent tunnelling medium, and its presence has considerably influenced the development of London, particularly during the nineteenth century. An examination of the map of the Underground railway system reveals that most of the routes run north of the Thames, in areas where London Clay either crops out, or is present beneath superficial deposits. More than 650 km of tunnels have been recorded beneath London. As well as underground railways, tunnels have been constructed for sewerage, the culverting of streams and rivers, roadways, water supply, electricity, telecommunications and civil defence. With increased demand for the limited space at the surface, it is likely that many more tunnels will be excavated in the future, for example for the routing of major electricity transmission lines.

Soft-ground tunnelling was pioneered in London in 1825, with Brunel's Rotherhithe to Wapping tunnel beneath the River Thames, which was built using a tunnelling shield to support the working face. A modern shield consists of a cylindrical steel shell, which is gradually moved forwards as tunnelling proceeds, allowing excavation and lining of the tunnel to proceed concurrently. A refinement, the digger shield, has a rotating cutter occupying the shield face; a digger shield may be able to advance the tunnel by nearly 2 m per hour. Tunnel linings today usually consist of reinforced concrete segments. Any space between the lining and the rock strata is normally grouted with concrete, and the joints between lining segments are also sealed to render the tunnel waterproof.

Generally, the London Clay is so impermeable that ingress of water during tunnelling is seldom a problem, although occasionally water entering through fissures has resulted in the digger shields becoming so clogged with sticky clay that the cutters cease to function. Tunnelling beneath the River Thames may require additional precautions; during the construction of the Blackwall Tunnel in the late nineteenth century, it was necessary to dump layers of clay on the river bed to prevent inundation. The most serious problems have resulted from the presence of water-bearing superficial deposits in local hollows penetrating far below the predicted upper surface of the London Clay; these features may be missed even with a very dense coverage of site-investigation boreholes prior to tunnelling. If an advancing face encounters such a deposit, gravel and water may rush into the tunnel and create a major subsidence cavity at the surface. Described by engineers as 'funnelling down', these deep, drift-filled hollows were encountered in the construction of the Post Office Railway in the vicinity of Mount Pleasant in 1924. During excavation of the Victoria Line in the 1960s, similar features were penetrated, leading to inundation of the tunnel and surface collapse. Beneath Green Park, the tunnel face unexpectedly broke into the gravel-fill of the former Tyburn valley, resulting in the complete burial of the digger shield and a major delay to the construction schedules.

If such features can be identified in advance of tunnelling, remedial measures can be taken. Injection of sodium silicate and calcium chloride solutions (the Joosten Process) is a successful and well-proved method. When injected into loose sand and gravel, the resultant chemical reaction produces calcium silicate, which cements the material into a weak 'sandstone'. This treatment method was used successfully in the 1930s, during the eastern extension of the Central Line between Stratford and Redbridge, and subsequently on many projects, where tunnels have penetrated superficial deposits. A number of other chemical injection techniques have been used successfully, for example in the construction of the second Blackwall Tunnel between 1960 and 1965. Ground freezing techniques have been used in a similar way to temporarily strengthen unconsolidated deposits, and are ideal for tackling localised areas of soft ground. However, the procedure is time-consuming and can take several months to render the deposit solid enough for excavation to proceed.

Where groundwater penetration was a particular problem, compressed air has been widely used to prevent the flow of water into the workings, as in the construction of the Dartford Tunnel and the second Blackwall Tunnel. The technique, first used in 1879, requires very strict medical and decompression procedures for the tunnellers. Working air pressures have to be varied, depending on the depth and type of strata encountered, and when the surrounding strata are particularly porous, it may be necessary to use chemical consolidation techniques in conjunction with the compressed air. Groundwater problems increase with depth, and are particularly serious where the arenaceous Lambeth Group and Thanet Sand Formation are encountered beneath the London Clay. At Euston, while tunnelling through the Woolwich and Reading formations for the Victoria Line, the use of compressed air had the deleterious side effect of displacing foul, deoxygenated air from within the sandy beds into nearby tunnel workings.

Ground surface settlement of a few centimetres is to be expected due to tunnelling operations, but modern practice keeps the effects to a minimum. The settlement is usually complete within a few days of tunnelling, and seldom causes any significant effect on buildings. However, during construction of the Victoria Line, elaborate underpinning measures were carried out at Oxford Circus in order to prevent damage to buildings with deep basements. After construction, ground pressure, particularly in the London Clay, may distort the tunnel lining, and some concrete tunnels have developed a slightly oval cross-section as a result.

Surface developments

As with tunnelling, many examples can be quoted of unexpected engineering problems related to the irregular rockhead surface, both in London and elsewhere. A typical case occurred in Victoria Street, London, where a drift-filled depression was encountered in excavations, which quickly became flooded. A major de-watering exercise was needed before construction could continue. Detailed site investigations should identify potential problems prior to construction, and enable preventative measures to be taken, for example, by extending sheet-piled retaining walls to below the base of such drift-filled hollows.

Many clays in the region are prone to swelling and shrinking, depending on changes in their moisture content. The consequent result, known as ground heave, can cause damage to buildings. Often the effects are very localised, caused for example by tree roots removing moisture, resulting in shrinkage of the clay. Conversely, the clearance of vegetation or disruption of land drains can increase moisture content in the clay, causing swelling. Widespread structural damage from these causes occurred following the drought in the summer of 1976. The clays of the Ancholme Group, and the Gault Formation are all affected, and the London Clay is particularly susceptible. This is reflected in the relatively high number of subsidence cases recorded from properties sited on London Clay.

The presence of acidity and high sulphate levels in groundwater can cause chemical reaction with tunnel linings, and can similarly cause damage to concrete foundations. Such aggressive water is commonly associated with Jurassic clays and parts of the London Clay, as a result of oxidation of pyrite. Beneath London, rising groundwater levels are likely to increase the risk of chemical and structural damage to tunnels and the foundations of buildings.

Potential subsidence caused by solution hollows is a well-known geological hazard affecting the Chalk outcrop. Rainwater containing dissolved carbon dioxide, can slowly dissolve the calcareous rock, particularly along joints and fissures, creating voids. Solution pipes and cavities, some several metres across, can be seen in chalk quarries in the Grays and Thurrock area of Essex. These features are generally infilled by material such as sand which has infiltrated from overlying deposits. In Watford, for example, shallow drift-filled voids in the chalk beneath river terrace deposits, have hindered construction projects. A number of cavities in the chalk, together with surface subsidence features related to collapse of such voids, were found during construction of the M40 motorway between Beaconsfield and High Wycombe. Due to their relatively small extent, such cavities can be difficult to locate during site investigations.

Man-made 'deneholes' within the chalk have long been associated with subsidence. The excavations, mostly dug to obtain flints in the past, typically consist of a shaft, up to 20 m in depth, connecting to caverns, which extend outwards from the shaft bottom as a series of chambers up to 5 m across. Deneholes are widespread in the Grays-Thurrock area, and over 130 have been recorded near Bexley. Two major collapses were recorded at Blackheath in 1881, following a period of heavy rainfall.

Landslipping is a geological hazard which occurs mainly on slopes of clay formations, particularly where these are overlain by water-bearing strata. The West Walton Formation and uppermost Oxford Clay where capped by Corallian formations in Oxfordshire and Wiltshire, and the Kimmeridge Clay where capped by the Portland Formation in Buckinghamshire, are commonly affected. The uppermost London Clay, beneath the sandy Claygate Member is particularly prone, for example in the cliffs west of Southend-on-Sea. Developers have generally avoided landslipped areas, which may be characterised by hummocky ground and unstable appearance, but if development is essential, then special techniques and foundation construction methods must be adopted. It is not unusual for minor failures to occur on man-made slopes, such as railway or road cuttings, many years after excavation.

High-tide levels on the coast and in London have been rising for a variety of reasons. The severe storm surge of 1953 flooded many parts of the east coast of England and London, emphasising the need to protect low-lying ground, by improving sea defences. More recently, concerns of global warming and rising world sea-levels, and the recognition that south-east England is gradually sinking, have increased the awareness of the risk of flooding in the long term. The major element in the flood defence strategy is the Thames Barrier, completed in 1984. The barrier, extending across the River Thames at Woolwich Reach, comprises movable gates which can be closed when exceptionally high tides are expected. The effects of rising sea-level were considered at the design stage, and the barrier is expected to protect London from flooding well into the 21st century.

References

The literature on the geology of the region is much too extensive to be given in full. The works listed below, together with their contained bibliographies, will provide a starting point for any reader interested in a particular topic. British Geological Survey memoirs for specific 1:50 000 sheet areas should also be consulted. Most of the references listed are held in the Library of the British Geological Survey, Keyworth, Nottingham. Copies of the references can be purchased subject to current copyright legislation.

Concealed rocks and basement structure (Chapter 2)

ALLSOP, J M, and SMITH, N J P. 1988. The deep geology of Essex. *Proceedings of the Geologists' Association*, Vol. 99, 249–260.

BRITISH GEOLOGICAL SURVEY. 1985. Pre-Permian geology of the UK (South). Scale 1:1 000 000. Two maps commemorating the 150th anniversary of the British Geological Survey. (Mitcham, Surrey: Cook, Hammond and Kell for the BGS on behalf of the Department of Energy.)

BULMAN, O M B, and RUSHTON, A W. 1973. Tremadoc faunas from boreholes in Central England. *Bulletin of the Geological Survey of Great Britain*, No. 43, 1–40.

BUTLER, D E. 1981. Marine faunas from concealed Devonian rocks of southern England and their reflection of the Frasnian transgression. *Geological Magazine*, Vol. 118, 679–697.

CHALONER, W G, and RICHARDSON, J B. 1977. South-east England. 26–40 *in* A correlation of the Devonian rocks of the British Isles. HOUSE, M R (editor). *Special Report of the Geological Society of London*, No. 8.

COCKS, L R M, HOLLAND, C H, and RICKARDS, R B. 1992. A revised correlation of Silurian rocks in the British Isles. *Special Report of the Geological Society of London*, No. 21.

FALCON, N L, and KENT, P E. 1960. Geological results of petroleum exploration in Britain 1945–1957. *Memoir of the Geological Society of London*, No. 2.

FOSTER, D, HOLLIDAY, D W, JONES, C M, OWENS, B, and WELSH, A. 1989. The concealed Upper Palaeozoic rocks of Berkshire and south Oxfordshire. *Proceedings of the Geologists' Association*, Vol. 100, 395–408.

MERRIMAN, R J, PHARAOH, T C, WOODCOCK, N H, and DALY, P. 1993. The metamorphic history of the concealed Caledonides of eastern England and their foreland. *Geological Magazine*, Vol. 130, 613–620.

MOLYNEUX, S G. 1991. The contribution of palaeontological data to an understanding of the early Palaeozoic framework of eastern England. *Annales de la Société Géologique de Belgique*, Vol. 114, 93–105.

WHITTAKER, A (editor). 1985. *Atlas of onshore sedimentary basins in England and Wales: post-Carboniferous tectonics and stratigraphy.* (Glasgow: Blackie.)

WOODCOCK, N H, and PHARAOH, T C. 1993. Silurian facies beneath East Anglia. *Geological Magazine*, Vol. 130, 681–690.

Jurassic (Chapters 3, 4 and 5)

ARKELL, W J, 1927. The Corallian rocks of Oxford, Berks and north Wilts. *Transactions of the Royal Society of London*, Vol. 216, 67–181.

ARKELL, W J, 1947. *The geology of Oxford.* (Oxford: Oxford University Press.)

BONEHAM, B F W, and WYATT, R J. 1993. The stratigraphical position of the Middle Jurassic (Bathonian) Stonesfield Slate of Stonesfield, Oxfordshire, U.K. *Proceedings of the Geologists' Association.* Vol. 104, 123–136.

BUCKMAN, S S. 1901. Bajocian and contiguous deposits in the north Cotteswolds: the main hill-mass. *Quarterly Journal of the Geological Society of London*, Vol. 57, 126–155.

CALLOMON, J H. 1955. The ammonite succession in the Lower Oxford Clay and Kellaways Beds at Kidlington, Oxfordshire, and the zones of the Callovian Stage. *Philosophical Transactions of the Royal Society of London*, Series B, Vol. 239, 215–264.

CALLOMON, J H. 1960. New sections in the Corallian Beds around Oxford, and the subzones of the *Plicatilis* Zone. *Proceedings of the Geologists' Association*, Vol. 71, 177–208.

CALLOMON, J H. 1968. The Kellaways Beds and the Oxford Clay. 264–290 in *The geology of the East Midlands.* SYLVESTER-BRADLEY, P C, and FORD, T D (editors). (Leicester: Leicester University Press.)

CAVE, R, and COX, B M. 1975. The Kellaways Beds of the area between Chippenham and Malmesbury, Wiltshire. *Bulletin of the Geological Survey of Great Britain*, No. 54, 41–66.

COPE, J C W (editor). 1980. A correlation of the Jurassic rocks of the British Isles. Part One: Introduction and Lower Jurassic. *Special Report of the Geological Society of London*, No. 15.

COPE, J C W (editor). 1980. A correlation of Jurassic rocks in the British Isles. Part Two: Middle and Upper Jurassic. *Special Report of the Geological Society of London*, No. 15.

COX, B M, HUDSON, J D, and MARTILL, D M. 1993. Lithostratigraphic nomenclature of the Oxford Clay (Jurassic). *Proceedings of the Geologists' Association*, Vol. 103, 343–345.

COX, B M, SUMBLER, M G, HORTON, A, and AMBROSE, K. 1991. Thicknesses of Kimmeridge Clay in the Oxford area. *Proceedings of the Geologists' Association*, Vol. 102, 145–148.

DEAN, W T, DONOVAN, D T, and HOWARTH, M K. 1961. The Liassic ammonite zones and subzones of the north-west European Province. *Bulletin of the British Museum (Natural History), Geology*, No. 4, 435–505.

DONOVAN, D T, HORTON, A, and IVIMEY-COOK, H C. 1979. The transgression of the Lower Lias over the northern flank of the London Platform. *Journal of the Geological Society of London*, Vol. 136, 165–173.

GALLOIS, R W, and COX, B M. 1977. The stratigraphy of the Middle and Upper Oxfordian sediments of Fenland. *Proceedings of the Geologists' Association*, Vol. 88, 207–228.

GALLOIS, R W, and WORSSAM, B C. 1983. Stratigraphy of the Harwell boreholes. *Report of the Fluid Processes Unit, Institute of Geological Sciences*, FLPU 83–14.

GREEN, G W, and DONOVAN, D T. 1969. The Great Oolite of the Bath area. *Bulletin of the Geological Survey of Great Britain*, No. 30, 1–88.

GREEN, G W, and MELVILLE, R V. 1956.   The stratigraphy of the Stowell Park Borehole (1949–51).   *Bulletin of the Geological Survey of Great Britain*, No. 11, 1–66.

HALLAM, A. 1968.   The Lias.   188–210 in *The geology of the East Midlands*. SYLVESTER-BRADLEY, P C, and FORD, T D (editors). (Leicester: Leicester University Press.)

MARTILL, D M, and HUDSON, J D (editors). 1991.   Fossils of the Oxford Clay. *Palaeontological Association Field Guide to Fossils*, No. 4.

MCKERROW, W S, and KENNEDY, W J. 1973.   The Oxford district.   *Geologists' Association Guide*, No. 3.

MORTER, A A. 1984.   Purbeck–Wealden mollusca and their relationship to ostracod biostratigraphy, stratigraphical correlation and palaeoecology in the Weald and adjacent areas.   *Proceedings of the Geologists' Association*, Vol. 95, 217–234.

OATES, M J. 1991.   Upper Kimmeridgian stratigraphy of Aylesbury, Buckinghamshire. *Proceedings of the Geologists' Assocation*, Vol. 100, 363–382.

PAGE, K N. 1989.   A stratigraphical revision for the English Lower Callovian. *Proceedings of the Geologists' Association*, Vol. 100, 363–382.

PALMER, T J. 1979.   The Hampen Marly and White Limestone Formations: Florida-type carbonate lagoons in the Jurassic of central England.   *Palaeontology*, Vol. 22, 189–228.

PALMER, T J, and JENKYNS H C. 1975.   A carbonate island barrier from the Great Oolite (Middle Jurassic) of central England.   *Sedimentology*, Vol. 22, 125–135.

PENN, I E, and WYATT, R G. 1979.   The stratigraphy and correlation of the Bathonian strata of the Bath–Frome area.   *Report of the Institute of Geological Sciences*, No. 78/22, 23–88.

POOLE, E G. 1969.   The stratigraphy of the Geological Survey Apley Barn Borehole, Witney, Oxfordshire.   *Bulletin of the Geological Survey of Great Britain*, No. 29, 1–103.

POOLE, E G. 1977.   The stratigraphy of the Steeple Aston Borehole, Oxfordshire. *Bulletin of the Geological Survey of Great Britain*, No. 57.

POOLE, E G. 1978.   The stratigraphy of the Withycombe Farm Borehole, near Banbury, Oxfordshire.   *Bulletin of the Geological Survey of Great Britain*, No. 68.

SELLWOOD, B W, and MCKERROW, W S. 1964.   Depositional environments in the lower part of the Great Oolite Group of Oxfordshire and north Gloucestershire. *Proceedings of the Geologists' Association*, Vol. 85, 189–210.

SUMBLER, M G. 1984.   The stratigraphy of the Bathonian White Limestone and Forest Marble Formations of Oxfordshire.   *Proceedings of the Geologists' Association*, Vol. 95, 51–64.

SUMBLER, M G. 1991.   The Fairford Coral Bed: new data on the White Limestone Formation (Bathonian) of the Gloucestershire Cotswolds.   *Proceedings of the Geologists' Association*, Vol. 102, 55–62.

SYLVESTER BRADLEY, P C. 1940.   The Purbeck Beds of Swindon.   *Proceedings of the Geologists' Association*, Vol. 51, 349–372.

SYLVESTER BRADLEY, P C. 1968.   The Inferior Oolite Series.   211–226 in *The geology of the East Midlands*. SYLVESTER BRADLEY, P C, and FORD, T D (editors). (Leicester: Leicester University Press.)

TORRENS, H S. 1967.   The Great Oolite Limestone of the Midlands.   *Transactions of the Leicester Literary and Philosophical Society*, Vol. 61, 65–90.

TORRENS, H S. 1968.   The Great Oolite Series.   227–263 in *The geology of the East Midlands*. SYLVESTER BRADLEY, P C, and FORD, T D (editors). (Leicester: Leicester University Press.)

TORRENS, H S. 1969. The stratigraphical distribution of Bathonian ammonites in Central England. *Geological Magazine,* Vol. 106, 63–76.

WIMBLEDON, W A, and COPE, J C W. 1978. The ammonite faunas of the English Portland Beds and the zones of the Portlandian Stage. *Journal of the Geological Society of London,* Vol. 135, 183–190.

WORSSAM, B C, and IVIMEY-COOK, H C. 1971. The stratigraphy of the Geological Survey Borehole at Warlingham, Surrey. *Bulletin of the Geological Survey of Great Britain,* No. 36, 1–146.

Cretaceous (Chapters 6 and 7)

ALLEN, P. 1981. Pursuit of Wealden models. *Journal of the Geological Society of London,* Vol. 138, 375–405.

BAILEY, H W, GALE, A S, MORTIMORE, R N, SWIECICKI, A, and WOOD, C J. 1983. The Coniacian–Maastrichtian stages of the United Kingdom, with particular reference to southern England. *Newsletters on Stratigraphy,* Vol. 12, 19–42.

BROMLEY, R G, and GALE, A S. 1982. The lithostratigraphy of the English Chalk Rock. *Cretaceous Research,* Vol. 3, 273–306.

CASEY, R. 1961. The stratigraphical palaeontology of the Lower Greensand. *Palaeontology,* Vol. 3, 487–622.

CASEY, R, and BRISTOW, C R. 1964. Notes on some ferruginous strata in Buckinghamshire and Wiltshire. *Geological Magazine,* Vol. 101, 116–128.

CLAYTON, C J. 1986. The chemical environment of flint formation in Upper Cretaceous chalks. 43–54 in *The scientific study of flint and chert (Proceedings of the Fourth International Flint Symposium, Brighton, 1983).* SIEVEKING, G DE G, and HART, M B (editors). (Cambridge: Cambridge University Press.)

GALE, A S, WOOD, C J, and BROMLEY, R G. 1987. The lithostratigraphy and marker bed correlation of the White Chalk (late Cenomanian–Campanian) in southern England. *Mesozoic Research,* Vol. 1, 107–118.

GALLOIS, R W, and MORTER, A A. 1982. The stratigraphy of the Gault of East Anglia. *Proceedings of the Geologists' Association,* Vol. 93, 351–368.

HANCOCK, J M. 1975. The petrology of the Chalk. *Proceedings of the Geologists' Association,* Vol. 86, 499–535.

HESSELBO, S P, COE, A L, BATTEN, D J, and WACH, G D. 1990. Stratigraphic relations of the Lower Greensand (Lower Cretaceous) of the Calne area, Wiltshire. *Proceedings of the Geologists' Association* Vol. 101, 265–278.

JARVIS, I. 1992. Sedimentology, geochemistry and origin of phosphatic chalks: the Upper Cretaceous deposits of NW Europe. *Sedimentology,* Vol. 39, 55–97.

JEFFERIES, R P S. 1963. The stratigraphy of the Actinocamax plenus Subzone (Lower Turonian) in the Anglo-Paris Basin. *Proceedings of the Geologists' Association,* Vol. 74, 1–33.

JUKES-BROWNE, A J, and HILL, W. 1900. The Cretaceous rocks of Britain. Vol. 1, The Gault and Upper Greensand of England. *Memoir of the Geological Survey of the Great Britain.*

JUKES-BROWNE, A J, and HILL, W. 1903. The Cretaceous rocks of Britain. Vol. 2, Lower and Middle Chalk of England. *Memoirs of the Geological Survey of the United Kingdom.*

JUKES-BROWNE, A J, and HILL, W. 1904. The Cretaceous rocks of Britain. Vol. 3, Upper Chalk of England. *Memoirs of the Geological Survey of the United Kingdom.*

KENNEDY, W J. 1969.   The correlation of the Lower Chalk of south-east England. *Proceedings of the Geologists' Association*, Vol. 80, 459–560.

KENNEDY, W J, and GARRISON, R E. 1975.   Morphology and genesis of nodular chalks and hardgrounds in the Upper Cretaceous of southern England.   *Sedimentology*, Vol. 22, 311–386.

MORTIMORE, R N. 1986.   Stratigraphy of the Upper Cretaceous White Chalk of Sussex.   *Proceedings of the Geologists' Association*, Vol. 97, 97–139.

MORTIMORE, R N. 1987.   Upper Cretaceous Chalk in the North and South Downs, England: a correlation.   *Proceedings of the Geologists' Association*, Vol. 98, 77–86.

MORTIMORE, R N. 1990.   Chalk or chalk.   15–45 in *Chalk*. (London: Thomas Telford.)

MORTIMORE, R N, and POMEROL, B. 1987.   Correlation of the Upper Cretaceous White Chalk (Turonian to Campanian) in the Anglo-Paris Basin.   *Proceedings of the Geologists' Association*, Vol. 98, 97–143.

MORTIMORE, R N, and WOOD, C J. 1986.   The distribution of flint in the English Chalk, with particular reference to the 'Brandon Flint Series' and the High Turonian flint maximum.   7–20 in *The scientific study of flint and chert (Proceedings of the Fourth International Flint Symposium, Brighton, 1983)*. SIEVEKING, G DE G, AND HART, M B (editors). (Cambridge: Cambridge University Press.)

OWEN, H G. 1971a.   Middle Albian stratigraphy in the Anglo-Paris Basin.   *Bulletin of the British Museum (Natural History), Geology*, Supplement 8.

OWEN, H G. 1971b.   The stratigraphy of the Gault in the Thames Estuary and its bearing on the Mesozoic tectonic history of the area.   *Proceedings of the Geologists' Association*, Vol. 82, 187–207.

OWEN, H G. 1972.   The Gault and its junction with the Woburn Sands in the Leighton Buzzard area, Bedfordshire and Buckinghamshire.   *Proceedings of the Geologists' Association*, Vol. 83, 287–312.

OWEN, H G. 1975.   The stratigraphy of the Gault and Upper Greensand of the Weald.   *Proceedings of the Geologists' Association*, Vol. 86, 475–498.

OWEN, H G. 1992.   The Gault–Lower Greensand Junction Beds in the northern Weald (England) and Wissant (France).   *Proceedings of the Geologists' Association*, Vol. 103, 83–110.

OWEN, E, and SMITH, A B (editors). 1987.   Fossils of the Chalk.   *Palaeontological Association Field Guide to Fossils*, No. 2.

RAWSON, P F, CURRY, D, DILLEY, F C, HANCOCK, J M, KENNEDY, W J, NEALE, J W, WOOD, C J, and WORSSAM, B C. 1978.   A correlation of Cretaceous rocks in the British Isles. *Special Report of the Geological Society of London*, No. 9.

ROBINSON, N D. 1986.   Lithostratigraphy of the Chalk Group of the North Downs, southeast England.   *Proceedings of the Geologists' Association*, Vol. 97, 141–170.

RUFFELL, A H. 1992.   Early to mid-Cretaceous tectonics and unconformities in the Wessex Basin (southern England).   *Journal of the Geological Society of London*, Vol. 149, 443–454.

SELLWOOD, B W , SCOTT, H, and LUNN, G. 1986.   Mesozoic basin evolution in southern England.   *Proceedings of the Geologists' Association*, Vol. 97, 259–289.

WOODS, M A, WILKINSON, I P, and HOPSON, P M. 1995.   The stratigraphy of the Gault Formation (Middle and Upper Albian) in the BGS Arlesey Borehole, Bedfordshire. *Proceedings of the Geologists' Association*, Vol. 106, 271–280.

Palaeogene and Neogene (Chapter 8)

AUBRY, M P, HAILWOOD, E A, and TOWNSEND, H A. 1986. Magnetic and calcareous-nannofossil stratigraphy of the lower Palaeogene formations of the Hampshire and London basins. *Journal of the Geological Society of London*, Vol. 143, 729–735.

BRISTOW, C R, ELLISON, R A, and WOOD, C J. 1980. The Claygate beds of Essex. *Proceedings of the Geologists' Association*, Vol. 91, 261–277.

BUURMAN, P. 1980. Palaeosols in the Reading Beds (Paleocene) of Alum Bay, Isle of Wight, U.K. *Sedimentology*, Vol. 27, 593–606.

CURRY, D. 1965. The Palaeogene beds of south-east England. *Proceedings of the Geologists' Association*, Vol. 76, 151–173.

CURRY, D. 1992. Tertiary. 389–411 in *Geology of England and Wales*. DUFF, P McL D and SMITH, A J (editors). (London: Geological Society of London.)

CURRY, D, ADAMS, C G, BOULTER, M C, DILLEY, F C, EAMES, F E, FUNNELL, B M, and WELLS, M K. 1978. A correlation of Tertiary rocks in the British Isles. *Special Report of the Geological Society of London*, No. 12.

DALEY, B. 1972. Some problems concerning the early Tertiary climate of southern Britain. *Palaeogeography, Palaeoclimatology, Palaeoecology*, Vol. 11, 177–190.

DAVIS, A G, and ELLIOTT, G F. 1958. The palaeogeography of the London Clay sea. *Proceedings of the Geologists' Association*, Vol. 68, 255–277.

ELLISON, R A. 1983. Facies distribution in the Woolwich and Reading Beds of the London Basin, England. *Proceedings of the Geologists' Association*, Vol. 94, 311–319.

ELLISON, R A, KNOX, R W O'B, JOLLEY, D W, and KING, C. 1994. A revision of the lithostratigraphical classification of the early Palaeogene strata of the London Basin and East Anglia. *Proceedings of the Geologists' Association*, Vol. 105, 187–197.

GIBBARD, P L, and ZALASIEWICZ, J A (editors). 1988. *Pliocene–Middle Pleistocene of East Anglia. Field Guide*. (Cambridge: Quaternary Research Association.)

JOLLEY, D W. 1992. Palynofloral association sequence stratigraphy of the Palaeocene Thanet Beds and equivalent sediments in eastern England. *Review of Palaeobotany and Palynology*, Vol. 74, 207–237.

HESTER, S W. 1965. Stratigraphy and palaeogeography of the Woolwich and Reading Beds. *Bulletin of the Geological Survey of Great Britain*, No. 23, 117–137.

HOOKER, J J, and INSOLE, A N. 1980. The distribution of mammals in the English Palaeogene. *Tertiary Research*, Vol. 3, 31–45.

KING, C. 1981. The stratigraphy of the London Clay and associated deposits. *Tertiary Research Special Paper*, Vol. 6. (Rotterdam: Backhuys.)

KNOX, R W, and ELLISON, R A. 1979. A Lower Eocene ash sequence in South–east England. *Quarterly Journal of the Geological Society of London*, Vol. 136, 251–253.

MATHERS, S J, and ZALASIEWICZ, J A 1988. The Red and Norwich Crags formations of southern East Anglia. *Proceedings of the Geologists' Association*, Vol. 99, 261–278.

MORTON, A C. 1982. The provenance and diagenesis of Palaeogene sandstones of south-east England as indicated by heavy mineral analysis. *Proceedings of the Geologists' Association*, Vol. 93, 263–274.

Quaternary (Chapter 9)

ALLEN, P, CHESHIRE, D A, and WHITEMAN, C A. 1991. Glacial deposits of southern East Anglia. 255–278 in *Glacial deposits in Great Britain and Ireland*. EHLERS, J, GIBBARD, P L, and ROSE, J (editors). (Rotterdam: A.A. Balkema.)

BALLANTYNE, C K, and HARRIS, C. 1994.   *The periglaciation of Great Britain.* (Cambridge: Cambridge University Press.)

BOWEN, D Q, HUGHES, S A, SYKES, G A, and MILLER, G M. 1989.   Land–sea correlations in the Pleistocene based on isoleucine epimerization in non-marine molluscs. *Nature, London,* Vol. 340, 49–51.

BOWEN, D Q, ROSE, J, MCCABE, A M, and SUTHERLAND, D G. 1986.   Correlation of Quaternary glaciations in England, Ireland, Scotland and Wales.   *Quaternary Science Reviews,* Vol. 5, 299–340.

BRIDGLAND, D R. 1988.   The Pleistocene fluvial stratigraphy and palaeogeography of Essex.   *Proceedings of the Geologists' Association,* Vol. 99, 291–314.

BRIDGLAND, D R. 1994.   *The Quaternary of the Thames.*   Geological Conservation Review Series. (London: Joint Nature Conservation Committee/Chapman and Hall.)

BRIDGLAND, D R, D'OLIER, B, GIBBARD, P L, and ROE, H M. 1993.   Correlation of Thames terrace deposits between the Lower Thames, eastern Essex and the submerged offshore continuation of the Thames–Medway valley.   *Proceedings of the Geologists' Association,* Vol. 104, 51–57.

BRIGGS, D J, COOPE, G R, and GILBERTSON, D D. 1985.   The chronology and environmental framework of early man in the Upper Thames valley: a new model. *British Archaeological Report,* No. 137.

DEVOY, R J N. 1977.   Flandrian sea level changes in the Thames estuary and the implications for land subsidence in England and Wales.   *Nature, London,* Vol. 270, 712–715.

DEVOY, R J N. 1979.   Flandrian sea level changes and vegetational history of the lower Thames estuary.   *Philosophical Transactions of the Royal Society of London,* Vol. B 285, 355–410.

GIBBARD, P L. 1977.   Pleistocene history of the Vale of St.Albans.   *Philosophical Transactions of the Royal Society of London,* Vol. B 280, 445–483.

GIBBARD, P L. 1985.   *The Pleistocene history of the Middle Thames Valley.*   (Cambridge: Cambridge University Press.)

GIBBARD, P L. 1994.   *Pleistocene history of the Lower Thames Valley.*   (Cambridge: Cambridge University Press.)

GREENSMITH, J T, and TUCKER, E V. 1971.   The effects of Late Pleistocene and Holocene sea-level changes in the vicinity of the River Crouch, East Essex.   *Proceedings of the Geologists' Association,* Vol. 82, 301–321.

GREENSMITH, J T, and TUCKER, E V. 1976.   Major Flandrian transgressive cycles, sedimentation and palaeogeography in the coastal zone of Essex, England.   *Geologie en Mijnbouw,* Vol. 55, 131–146.

GREENSMITH, J T, and TUCKER, E V. 1980.   Evidence for differential subsidence on the Essex coast.   *Proceedings of the Geologists' Association,* Vol. 91, 169–175.

HEY, R W. 1986.   A re-examination of the Northern Drift of Oxfordshire. *Proceedings of the Geologists' Association,* Vol. 97, 291–302.

IMBRIE, J, HAYS, J D, MARTINSON, D G, MCINTYRE, A, MIX, A C, MORLEY, J J, PISIAS, N G, PRELL, W L, and SHACKLETON, N J. 1984.   The orbital theory of Pleistocene climate: support from a revised chronology of the marine $\delta^{18}O$ record.   269–305 in *Milankovitch and climate Part 1.* BERGER A (editor). (Hingham, Massachusets: D. Reidel Publishing.)

IMBRIE, J, and IMBRIE, K P. 1979.   Ice ages: solving the mystery.   (London: Macmillan Press.)

JONES, R L, and KEEN, D H. 1993. *Pleistocene environments in the British Isles.* (London: Chapman and Hall.)

MARSLAND, A. 1986. The flood plain deposits of the Lower Thames. *Quarterly Journal of Engineering Geology,* Vol. 19, 223–247.

MEGAW, J V S, and SIMPSON, D D A. 1979. *Introduction to British prehistory.* (Leicester: Leicester University Press.)

MOLLESON, T. 1977. Skeletal remains of man in the British Quaternary. 3–92 in *British Quaternary studies: recent advances.* SHOTTON, F W (editor). (Oxford: Clarendon Press.)

MORRISON, A. 1980. *Early Man in Britain and Ireland.* (London: Croom Helm.)

OAKLEY, K P. 1952. Swanscombe Man. *Proceedings of the Geologists' Association,* Vol. 63, 271–300.

ROE, D A. 1981. *The Lower and Middle Palaeolithic Periods in Britain.* (London: Routledge and Kegan Paul.)

SHOTTON, F W (editor). 1977. *British Quaternary studies: recent advances.* (Oxford: Clarendon Press.)

SMART, P L, and FRANCES, P D (editors). 1991. Quaternary dating methods — a user's guide. *Quaternary Research Association Technical Guide,* No. 4.

STUART, A J. 1988. *Life in the Ice Age.* (Princes Risborough: Shire Publications.)

SUMBLER, M G. 1995. The terraces of the rivers Thame and Thames and their bearing on the chronology of glaciation in central and eastern England. *Proceedings of the Geologists' Association,* Vol. 106, 93–106.

WHITEMAN, C A. 1992. The palaeogeography and correlation of pre-Anglian glaciation terraces of the River Thames in Essex and the London Basin. *Proceedings of the Geologists' Association,* Vol. 103, 37–56.

WHITEMAN, C A, and ROSE, J. 1992. Thames river sediments of the British Early and Middle Pleistocene. *Quaternary Science Reviews,* Vol. 11, 363–375.

WYMER, J J. 1968. *Lower Palaeolithic archaeology in Britain as represented by the Thames Valley.* (London: John Baker.)

WYMER, J J. 1977. The archaeology of man in the British Quaternary. 93–106 in *British Quaternary studies: recent advances.* SHOTTON, F W (editor). (Oxford: Clarendon Press.)

WYMER, J J. 1991. *Mesolithic Britain.* (Princes Risborough: Shire Publications.)

Geology and man (Chapter 10)

ARKELL, W J. 1947. *Oxford stone.* (London: Faber and Faber.)

BONIFACE, E S. 1959. Some experiments with artificial recharge in the lower Lea Valley. *Proceedings of the Institution of Civil Engineers,* Vol. 14, 325–338.

BRITISH GEOLOGICAL SURVEY. 1995. *United Kingdom Minerals Yearbook, 1994.* (Keyworth, Nottingham: British Geological Survey.)

CRAIG, R N, and SIMPSON, B. 1990. Potential problems associated with rising groundwater levels in the deep aquifer beneath London. Tunnel Construction '90, *Institution of Mining and Metallurgy Special Publication,* 1–8.

DOWNING, R A. 1990. Hydrology of the Chalk in the UK: the evolution of our understanding. *Proceedings of the International Chalk Symposium,* Brighton. 550–570.

EDMUNDS, W M, DARLING, W G, KINNIBURGH, D G, DEVER, L, and VACHIER, P. 1992. Chalk groundwater in England and France: hydrogeochemistry and water quality. *British Geological Survey Reseach Report* SD/92/2.

EDWORTHY, K J, and DOWNING, R A. 1979. Artificial groundwater recharge and its relevance in Britain. *Journal of the Institution of Water Engineers and Scientists*, Vol. 33, 151–172.

HARRIS, P M. 1993. Review of information on onshore sand and gravel resources in England. *British Geological Survey Technical Report* WA/93/35.

HARRIS, P M, HIGHLEY, D E, HILLIER, J, and WHITWOOD, A. 1994. *Directory of mines and quarries.* Fourth edition. (Keyworth, Nottingham: British Geological Survey.)

HIGGINBOTTOM, I E, AND FOOKES, P G. 1971. Engineering aspects of periglacial features in Britain. *Quarterly Journal of Engineering Geology*, Vol. 3, 85–117.

INESON, J. 1962. A hydrogeological study of the permeability of the Chalk. *Journal of the Institution of Water Engineers and Scientists*, Vol. 16, 449–463.

MEGAW, T M. 1970. Bored tunnels through water bearing strata in urban conditions in England. *Proceedings of 6th National Tunnel Symposium, Japan Society of Civil Engineers*, 47–66.

MOORLOCK, B S P, and HIGHLEY, D E. 1991. An appraisal of fuller's earth resources in England and Wales. *British Geological Survey Technical Report* WA/91/75.

NATIONAL RIVERS AUTHORITY. 1993. *Policy and practice for the protection of groundwater.* (Bristol: National Rivers Authority.)

PRICE, M, DOWNING, R A, and EDMUNDS, W M. 1993. The Chalk as an aquifer. 35–58 in *The hydrogeology of the Chalk of north–west Europe.* DOWNING, R A. PRICE, M, and JONES, G P (editors). (Oxford: Clarendon Press.)

ROBINSON, E. 1984. *London: illustrated geological walks. Book 1.* (Edinburgh: Scottish Academic Press.)

ROBINSON, E. 1985. *London: illustrated geological walks. Book 2.* (Edinburgh: Scottish Academic Press.)

SMITH, D B, DOWNING, R A, MONKHOUSE, R A, OTLET, R L, and PEARSON, F L. 1976. The age of groundwater in the Chalk of the London Basin. *Water Resources Research*, Vol. 12, 392–404.

WATER RESOURCES BOARD. 1972. *The hydrogeology of the London Basin.* (Reading: Water Resources Board.)

BRITISH GEOLOGICAL SURVEY MAPS

British Geological Survey maps and associated literature are available from the Sales Desk, British Geological Survey, Keyworth NG12 5GG (telephone 0115 936 3100), through the British Geological Survey London Information Office, Natural History Museum (Earth Galleries), South Kensington, London SW7 (telephone 0171 589 4090), or through HMSO stockists and all good booksellers. A catalogue of maps and literature is available on request.

Recommended small–scale geological maps include:

1:625 000 (about 10 miles to one inch)
Geological map of the United Kingdom (Solid Geology), South, 1979
Quaternary map of the United Kingdom, South, 1977

1:250 000 (about 4 miles to one inch)

East Midlands (Solid Geology) 1983
Bristol Channel (Solid Geology) 1988
Chilterns (Solid Geology) 1991
Thames Estuary (Solid Geology) 1989

Medium-scale maps:

Almost all of the region is covered by 1:50 000-scale or 1:63 360-scale (one mile to one inch) geological maps; these generally show both solid and drift (Quaternary) geology. An explanatory memoir is available for most of these maps; in the case of those out of print, copies can be obtained through libraries.

Index

Printed in the United Kingdom for HMSO
Dd 301328 5/96 C80